An introduction to

Bench fitting

Published by
EnTra Publications
Vector House
41 Clarendon Road
Watford WD1 1HS

Foreword & Acknowledgements

This book provides a basic introduction to bench fitting as practised in an engineering workshop. Its purpose is to give a general appreciation and understanding of the various tools and techniques. It will also provide a future source of reference and a valuable reminder of correct methods.

The book should be used as support material for anyone starting on a course of practical instruction in an engineering environment.

In particular, the book covers the knowledge required to achieve **Unit No. P06054G2 Basic bench fitting** of the National Vocational Qualification in Engineering Manufacture (Foundation) at Level 2. It should be noted, however, that some of the information given in this book goes beyond the level of knowledge required to satisfy the assessor for the NVQ unit.

Acknowledgements

We wish to acknowledge the following contributions to the production of this book:

Roger L.Timings for sourcing and writing much of the material

Keith Francis for his constructive comments on the manuscript

Longman Group (UK) Ltd for permission under a reciprocal agreement to reproduce and adapt some of their drawings.

Contents

4

Hand tools

Bench fitting involves the use of a wide range of hand tools. This section describes those most commonly encountered and gives details of the correct methods of using them.

Hand tools - the workbench

The workbench

The workbench should always be kept clean and tidy.

All tools should have a clearly identified storage place and only the tools required for the particular job in hand should be on the workbench.

Drawers and tool cupboards should also be kept tidy. This is necessary to enable you to find tools quickly, but it is also important for your safety and to prevent tools becoming damaged.

The floor surrounding the workbench must be kept clean and clear from obstructions. It is particularly important that any oil or grease is cleaned up immediately.

Use separate bins for different types of waste - follow the laid down practice for your workshop.

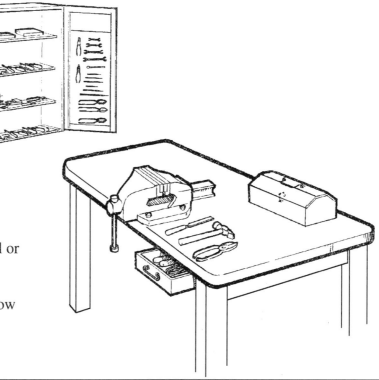

Vices

Most fitting benches have a vice permanantly fixed.

The fitter uses a vice to hold work safely and securely while carrying out such operations as sawing, chiselling and filing. A typical parallel jaw vice is shown in the illustration. It is fitted with a quick release trigger so that you can adjust the position of the jaws quickly and only use the screw and handle for the final tightening. The vice jaws are designed to give maximum grip but unfortunately they also tend to mark the workpiece.

The fixed jaw should be just clear of the front edge of the bench so that when long work is being held it can hang down clear of the bench.

It is important that the bench and the vice are at a suitable height to avoid strain and excessive back bending. Experience shows that the most comfortable height is when the vice jaws are level with your elbow - see illustration.

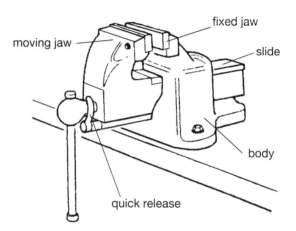

Hand tools - vices

Positioning work

Work should be positioned in the vice so that the major forces acting on the work are directed towards the fixed jaw. For example, when using a chisel the hammer should be driving the chisel through the work towards the fixed jaw.

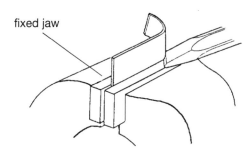

fixed jaw

The work should be held in the vice so that the point being worked upon is as close to the jaws as possible. If it is too far from the jaws there is a danger that the workpiece will bend under the applied force.

When using a hacksaw to cut material held in a vice it may be necessary to reposition the work in the jaws several times to keep the cutting position close to the jaws. If this is not done the material will vibrate and produce an irritating and unnecessary noise.

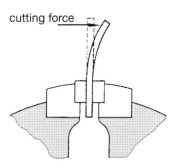

cutting force

work positioned too high in the vice - workpiece bends and vibrates

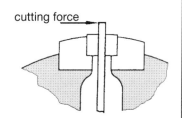

cutting force

work positioned lower in the vice - reduced leverage prevents the workpiece bending or vibrating

Hand tools - vices

Vice jaws

The jaws of a fitter's vice are made of steel with serrations cut into them to give a firm grip on the workpiece. They can be replaced by smooth steel jaws or jaws made of a softer material (brass, copper, fibre etc) if it is necessary to avoid marking the workpiece.

Vice shoes

Vice shoes can be used instead of replacement jaws. These are slipped over the serrated jaws when required. Vice shoes can be made from soft metal, such as brass, copper or aluminium, or some suitable fibrous or plastic material.

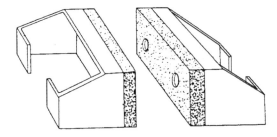

Files

Files are used for the removal of metal. In skilled hands they can produce accurate surfaces with a good finish.

Files are made from hardened steel and the teeth are cut into the body in various patterns depending upon the intended use.

There are four features of a file which are used to describe it:

- the length
- the type of cut
- the grade of cut
- the shape.

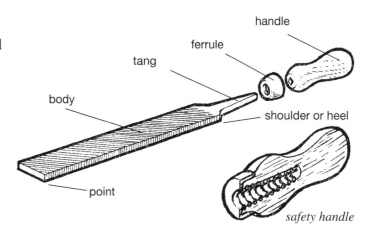

safety handle

File length

The length of a file is measured from the point to the shoulder.

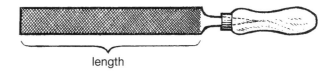

length

11

Hand tools - files

Type of cut

The most commonly used cuts are single,
double and rasp.

Single cut
The single cut file is used on softer metals
such as brass and copper. As there is only
one set of teeth the file is less likely to clog.

Double cut
The double cut file is used on iron and steel
and is the most commonly used file in
general engineering. As its name implies it
has two sets of teeth crossing each other.

Rasp
The rasp is used for filing very soft metals
and non-metals such as wood and plastics.

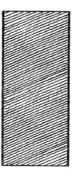  

single cut　　　*double cut*　　　*rasp*

Hand tools - files

Grade of cut

The grade of a file is determined by the spacing of the teeth. This applies to both single and double cut files. There are five grades but not all grades are available for each shape.

Rough cut
Used for preliminary filing to remove metal quickly.

Bastard cut
A semi-rough grade used where a good finish is not required.

Second cut
A finer grade used to cut fairly quickly and give a medium finish.

Smooth cut
Used to give a better finish where only small amounts of metal need to be removed.

Dead smooth cut
Used only for final finishing with minimal metal removal.

rough

bastard

second cut

smooth

File shape

Various shapes and section of file are available, each being suited to a different type of work.

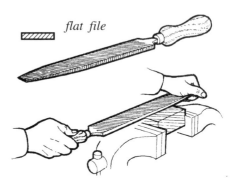

flat file

Flat file
This is used for general surfacing work. Both faces are double cut and both edges are single cut. It is tapered in width and thickness for the last third of its length.

Ward file
This is used for filing narrow slots. Both faces are double cut and both edges are single cut. It is tapered in width but not in thickness.

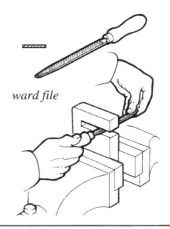

ward file

Hand tools - files

Hand file

This is parallel in width but tapers slightly in thickness. It is used for level filing and general flat work. It is usually double cut on both faces and single cut on one edge only. The remaining edge is left uncut and is called a "safe edge". The safe edge is essential when working up to a finished or semi-finished surface on a stepped component.

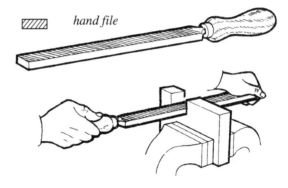

hand file

Pillar file

This is used in narrow slots. Both faces are double cut and either both edges are single cut or one edge is left uncut to provide a safe edge. Unlike the ward file, the pillar file is parallel throughout its length. It is also thicker and stronger than a ward file.

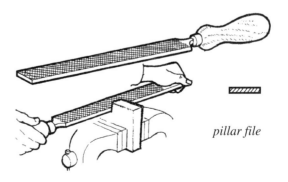

pillar file

15

Hand tools - files

Square file
As its name implies this file is square in section. It tapers on all sides for about a third of its length. It is used to file rectangular holes, slots and grooves. It is usually double cut on all sides.

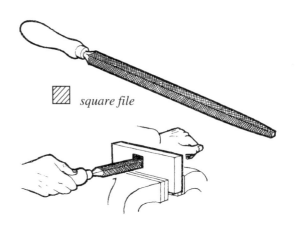

square file

Round file
This is used for opening out holes and rounding inside corners. Rough, bastard, second cut and smooth files under 150mm length are single cut.

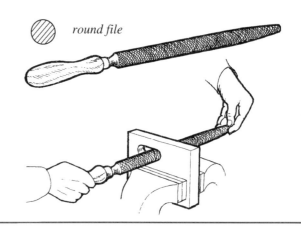

round file

Hand tools - files

Half-round file

The flat side of a half-round file is used for general work and the half-round side is used for filing concave surfaces. It is double cut on the flat side. The curved side is single cut and graded smooth or second cut.

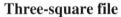 half-round file

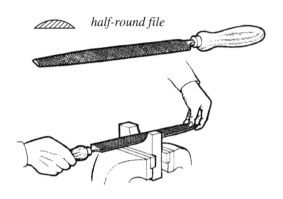

Three-square file

Sometimes called a triangular file. The section of a three-square file is an equilateral triangle (all the sides are the same length). It is used for filing corners between 60° and 90°. It is double cut on all sides.

three-square file

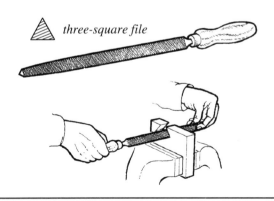

Hand tools - files

Mill saw file
This file has half-round edges and its primary use is for sharpening saw blades.

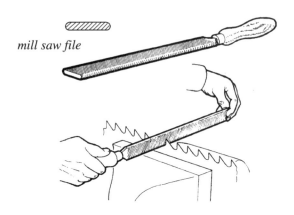

mill saw file

Rasp
The rasp is flat on one side and curved on the other. It is used on soft metals, wood and other soft, non-metallic substances.

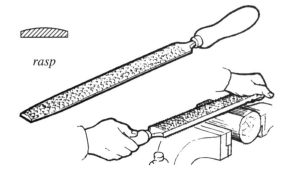

rasp

File handles

Handles are made of wood or plastic. Wooden handles have a metal ferrule to prevent the handle splitting. Do not use a wooden handle without a ferrule.

metal ferrule

The handle may have a small hole drilled in it to take the file tang. In this case, insert the tang into the hole and gently tap the handle on the bench until the tang is securely gripped by the handle. If the handle is supplied without a hole, a hole of the appropriate size should be drilled. Care must be taken not to split the handle during this operation.

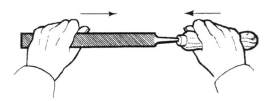

SAFETY NOTE

A file must always be fitted with a handle. It is extremely dangerous to use a file without a handle as the tang can easily penetrate the hand or the wrist causing a severe injury.

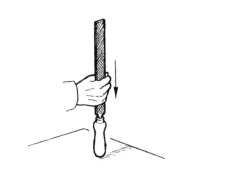

Using files

It is important to select the correct file for the particular job. Use a large file for large areas and a small file for thin sections. Use a coarse file when a large amount of metal has to be removed and a smoother file when removing only small amounts or when a good finish is required.

For accurate filing with minimum effort you must adopt the correct stance. The pressure on the file is varied during the stroke to keep the cut even (see illustrations below) and the body weight must be distributed evenly to retain balance throughout the stroke.

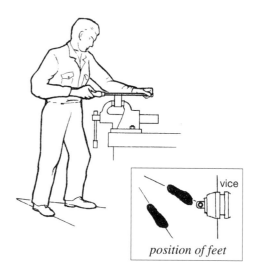

position of feet

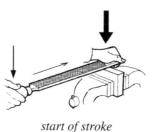

start of stroke

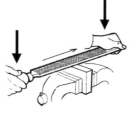

mid-stroke

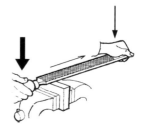

end of stroke

20

Hand tools - files

Cross filing

Cross filing is used to produce a flat surface. The file is used at an angle of approximately 45° to the workpiece and the aim should be to cover as large an area as possible with each stroke. After a few strokes, repeat the filing at approximately 90° to the original direction.

To maintain flatness and keep the file clean, the file should not be lifted on the return stroke.

The workpiece should be checked frequently for flatness. The high spots are then filed down and the workpiece rechecked until the required standard of flatness is achieved.

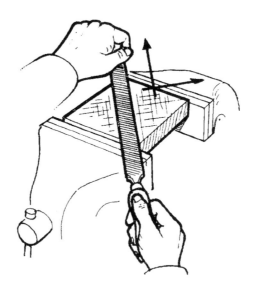

Hand tools - files

Draw filing

This method is used to remove rough file marks and to produce a good surface finish. A smooth file should be used at 90° to the workpiece and held as shown in the illustration. Your hands should be as close to the workpiece as possible; this gives better control. The filing action is to push and pull the file along the length of the workpiece.

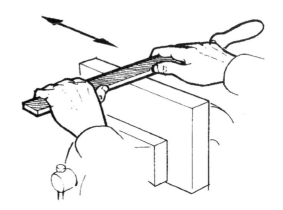

Filing large surfaces

Use a file holder if the surface to be filed is larger than the file.

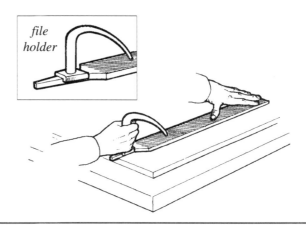

file holder

Hand tools - files

Cleaning files

During filing small particles of metal can become embedded in the teeth of the file. This causes rough file marks known as "pinning". To avoid this, regular cleaning should be carried out with a special wire brush called a file card.

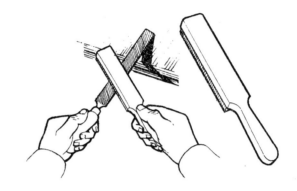

Particles which resist removal with a file card can often be dislodged with a thin piece of soft metal.

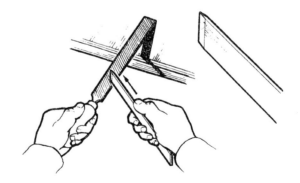

For finishing work, soft chalk rubbed into the spaces between the teeth of the file helps to prevent pinning.

Hand tools - files

Protection of workpieces

Once the first surface of the workpiece has been finished, care must be taken to protect that finish when further work is carried out. The workpiece must be handled carefully. If the workpiece is to be held in a vice or in clamps, soft jaws or soft metal protectors should be used. If a hammer has to be used on the workpiece it should be rawhide or soft faced. Finished faces need to be protected by some sort of shield if there is any danger of tool slip.

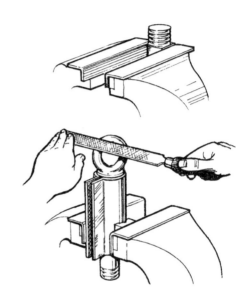

Storage of files

To avoid blunting the teeth or breaking the files, they should be stored carefully in a tool box or rack and out of contact with each other or other tools.

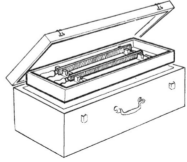

Hacksaws

A hacksaw is a hand saw for cutting metal.

It consists of a frame and a blade. The frame may be adjustable in length. The blade is fitted into the frame with the teeth pointing away from the handle. The tension of the blade can be adjusted using the wing nut.

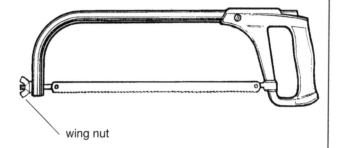

wing nut

Junior hacksaws are not adjustable and the blade is tensioned by the spring of the frame. The blades are carbon steel and flexible. They are used for small work where a conventional hacksaw would be unwieldy.

junior hacksaw

SAFETY - points to check before use:
* the blade should not be twisted
* there should be NO blunt or broken teeth
* the blade should not be discoloured (this indicates that it is softer than it should be)
* the teeth should face the direction of the cut.

Take great care if you have to use a new blade in an existing cut - it is likely to jam.

Hacksaw blades

Blades for a conventional hacksaw are made of high speed steel. They are available in two types: "all-hard" and "flexible".

All-hard blades
These are hardened throughout. They are very rigid and in the hands of an experienced operator will give an accurate cut and a long blade life.

Flexible blades
These blades are hardened on the cutting edge only. They are unbreakable in normal use and are intended for the inexperienced operator or where the awkward nature of the work is liable to cause breakage of the all-hard type. They give a less accurate cut than the all-hard type of blade (because of their flexibility) and they wear quicker.

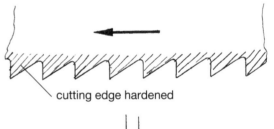

cutting edge hardened

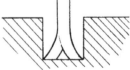

The teeth of a hacksaw blade are set so that the blade cuts a slot wider than itself.

The blade must be at the correct tension to keep the cut accurate and minimise the risk of blade breakage.

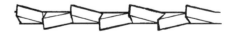

Hand tools - hacksaws

A hacksaw blade is classified by the number of teeth per unit length. This is usually stated as the number of teeth in a length of 25mm. However, blades are sometimes marked with the number of teeth per inch, often abbreviated to TPI. As an inch is very nearly the same length as 25mm there is no significant difference between the two systems of classification.

For hand hacksaws:
• coarse blades have 14 to 18 teeth per 25mm
• fine blades have 24 to 32 teeth per 25mm.

Thick materials should be cut with a coarse blade and thin materials with a finer blade. Choose a blade which is fine enough to ensure that at least three teeth are in contact with the material when a cut is being made.

If the teeth of a blade become clogged use a coarser blade. Soft materials such as aluminium are particularly likely to cause clogging.

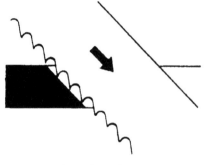

at least 3 teeth in contact

Hand tools - hacksaws

Using a hacksaw

The workpiece should be firmly held in a vice.

Hold the hacksaw at an angle of about 30° and make a few short backward and forward strokes on the workpiece to start the cut. Then, using both hands on the saw as illustrated, continue cutting with a steady rhythm using full length strokes.

The rate of sawing should be 40-50 stokes per minute and cutting pressure should only be applied on the forward strokes.

When cutting thin material, the saw should be held at a shallow angle to the length of the cut to increase the number of teeth in contact with the material. This stops the blade snatching. If a very thin material is to be cut, it is a good idea to sandwich it between two pieces of wood to prevent it from twisting or bending.

When cutting pipework or tubing, mark a guideline round the workpiece and rotate it at intervals during the cutting process.

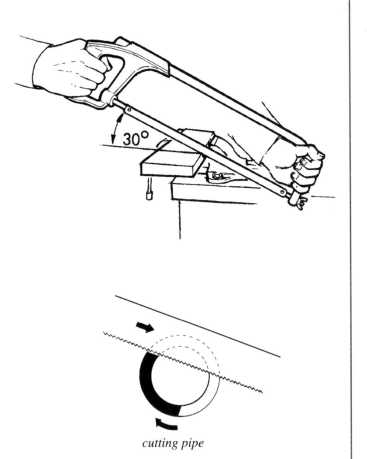

cutting pipe

Hand tools - hacksaws

With the blade in the normal position, the depth to which the hacksaw can cut is limited by the distance between the blade and the back of the frame. However, the pin holders at both ends of the frame can be rotated through a right angle and this enables the blade to be mounted at 90° to its usual position.

With the blade like this, it is possible to make unlimited lengths of cut provided that the width of the piece being cut off is not greater than the distance between the blade and the back of the frame - see illustration.

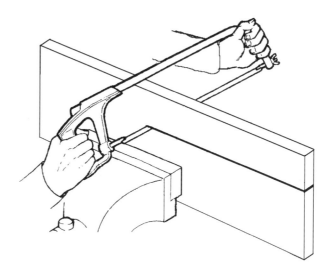

Hammers

A hammer consists of a head and a shaft. The head is usually made of cast steel with the striking face and the pein hardened and tempered. The shaft can be either wood or steel and a hand grip of rubber or plastic may be fitted.

The shaft must be of an appropriate size for the head. It must fit the head and be adequately secured. Wooden shafts should be secured with one or more wedges. A hammer with a loose head, a chipped face, or a split shaft must never be used.

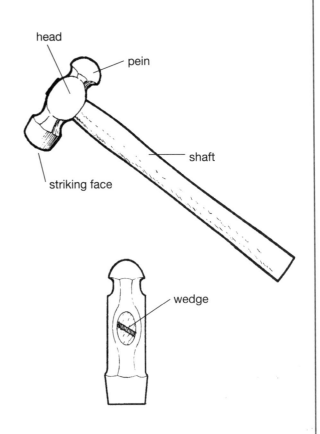

SAFETY - before using a hammer always check that:

- the handle is not split

- the head is securely fitted

- the head is not cracked or chipped.

Hand tools - hammers

Hammers are classified by the shape of head and by weight.

A ball pein hammer is the type most commonly used by a fitter. Cross pein and straight pein hammers are used in awkward places where a ball pein could not reach.

Hand hammers vary in weight between 100g (3½ ounces) and 1.5kg (3lb). The most useful weight range is 200g to 500g.

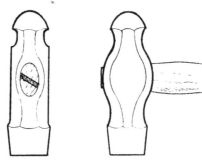

ball pein hammer

cross pein hammer

straight pein hammer

Hand tools - hammers

Using hammers

A hammer should be held in a firm grip at the end of the shaft.

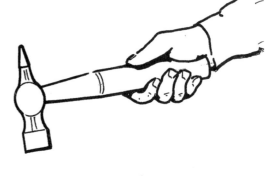

A hammer can be used in conjunction with another tool such as a centre punch or a chisel.

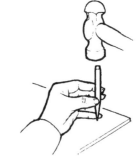

It can also be used in direct contact with the work, such as driving in a key - see illustration. Sometimes a piece of softer material is held between the hammer and the work to prevent bruising. Wood or brass are often used for this purpose.

Hand tools - hammers

A hammer face should be kept free from burrs and blemishes by rubbing it on fine emery cloth.

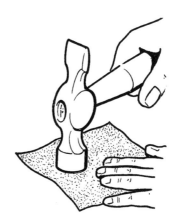

There are also soft hammers (mallets) faced with various materials such as rubber, plastic, rawhide, copper or brass. These are used to work on finished surfaces when it is necessary to prevent damage.

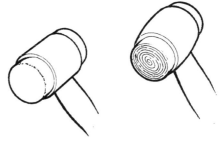

Hand tools - punches

Punches

Punches are used for making indentations or dots in the workpiece. These indentations are used for marking out, as witness marks and to guide and start the points of drills.

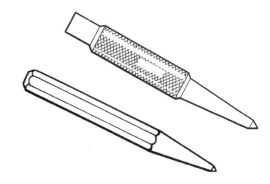

Centre punches

A centre punch has its point ground to an included angle of 90°. Its main use is for marking the centres of holes to be drilled and serves as a start for the drill point.

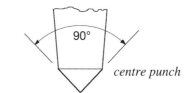

centre punch

Dot punches

A dot punch is used in marking out to emphasise lines and as a locator for the point of dividers when drawing arcs and circles. The point of a dot punch is normally ground to an included angle of 60°, but an angle of 40° is sometimes used for fine precision work.

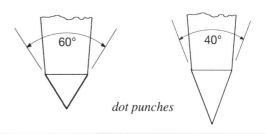

dot punches

Hand tools - punches

Using punches

- Hold the punch at an angle so that the position of the point can be seen clearly and set the point where the punch mark is required.

- Bring the punch to a position at a right angle to the surface to be marked, making sure that the point does not move from the required position.

- Strike the end of the punch lightly with a hammer, taking care that the hammer hits the punch squarely.

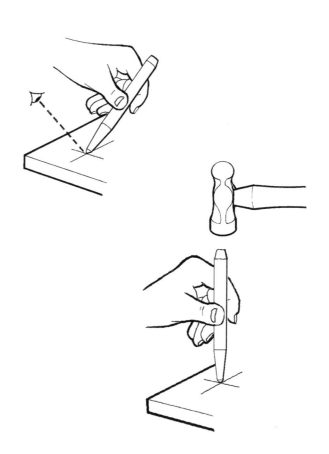

When using a punch always check that:

- the point of the punch is sharp

- the head of the punch is not chipped or mushroomed.

Cold chisels

A cold chisel driven by hammer blows is used to chip away metal in the cold state. In the past, chipping with a chisel occupied much of the fitter's time. Today machining is used for the bulk removal of surplus metal and chipping is only used when it is not possible to use a machine.

SAFETY when chipping with a cold chisel.

- The cold chisel should always be directed away from the body.

- Never use a chisel with a mushroomed head - pieces of metal may fly off when the chisel is struck with a hammer.

- Never chip towards another person.

- Goggles and a chipping screen must always be used.

mushroomed heads are dangerous

Hand tools - cold chisels

A cold chisel is made from high quality steel. The cutting edge is hardened and tempered. The remainder of the chisel is left unhardened so that it is less brittle and able to withstand hammer blows without fracturing.

Chisel point angles vary between 30° and 60°. The sharper angled tools are used for chipping softer metals.

Chisels are identified by their length and the type and width of cutting edge. They are made in lengths from 100mm upwards. The main types of cutting edge are flat, crosscut, round nose and diamond point.

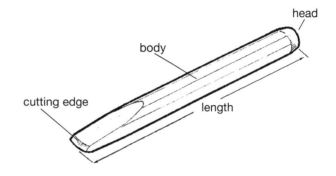

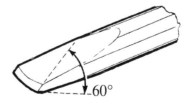

chisel point angle

37

Chisel shape

Flat chisel
This is a general purpose cutting tool and is the type most often used.

The flat chisel should be held firmly but lightly at an angle of 30° to 40° to the cutting plane. Position yourself so that you can watch the cutting edge.

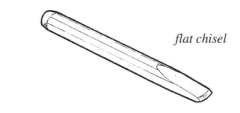

flat chisel

When the chisel is used to cut sheet metal you should put wood or other soft material under the sheet being cut. Holes may be cut in the waste part of the material to relieve the pressure on the outer edge. The cutting edge of the chisel should be "angled" onto the work surface to obtain a continuous line of cut.

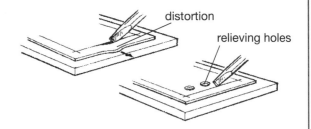

distortion

relieving holes

The flat chisel can also be used to cut rods and bars, to chip excess metal from large surfaces and to cut off rivet heads and rusted nut and bolt heads.

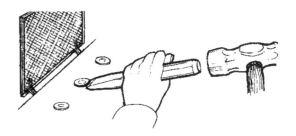

Hand tools - cold chisels

Crosscut chisel

This is used to cut parallel grooves and to break up large areas into narrow sections which can then be cut away with a flat chisel. The work should be reversed when getting near the far edge to prevent the edge from breaking away.

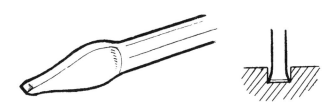

The cutting edge is slightly wider than the rest of the body to prevent the body from binding in the groove which has been cut.

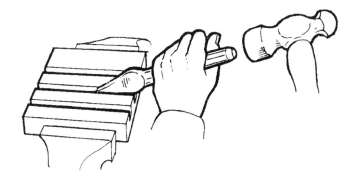

Hand tools - cold chisels

Round nose chisel
This is used to cut grooves and oil channels in bearings and bushes.

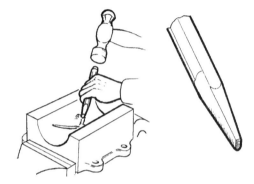

Diamond point chisel
This is used to cut vee grooves in metal, to chip through plate, to clean out internal angles and to square up corners of slots.

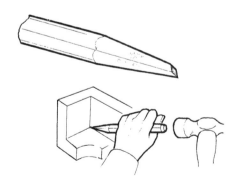

Hand tools - cold chisels

Chiselling large areas

When a large area has to be chiselled, first cut grooves with a crosscut chisel, then remove the strips in-between the grooves using a flat chisel.

The work should be reversed when getting near the far edge to stop the edge being broken away.

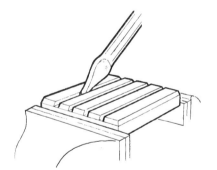

cut grooves with a crosscut chisel

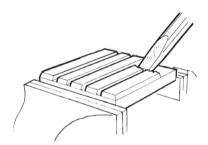

remove strips with a flat chisel

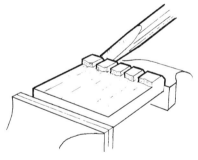

reverse the work towards the end

For details of sharpening chisels and removing mushroomed heads, see the later section on off-hand grinding.

Hand tools - spanners

Spanners

Spanners are used to hold or turn nuts and the heads of screws and bolts. There are many types of spanner, each intended for use in different circumstances.

They are usually made from high tensile steel forgings and often kept in sets covering a range of sizes. Each spanner head is marked with its size and (except for some metric spanners) there will also be an indication of the screw thread system for which it is intended.

Although ISO Metric threads are now widespread throughout British engineering, there are many other thread systems in use. You are likely to come across several systems, particularly in maintenance work.

It is important that you always use a spanner made for the particular thread system on which you are working. A spanner made for a different system is unlikely to fit properly - this could damage the workpiece and cause you injury.

Some common screw thread systems

Name	Abbreviation
ISO Metric	M
Unified Coarse	UNC
Unified Fine	UNF
Whitworth	W
British Standard Fine	BSF or BS
British Association	BA
British Standard Pipe	BSP

Hand tools - spanners

Sizes of spanner

Metric spanners are sized by the dimension in millimetres across the flats of the nut they are made to fit. The number is marked adjacent to the head of the spanner. It may be shown just as a number, or it may have **M** or **mm** with the number.

Some spanners made in imperial (inch) sizes are also sized by the dimension across the flats of the appropriate nut. This is usually shown as a fraction (of an inch) and is followed by either **AF** or **A/F**.

Spanners made to fit the Whitworth and British Standard Fine screw thread systems are sized by the diameter in inches of the thread onto which the nut fits. This is shown as a fraction which is followed by the abbreviation for the thread system. Note that a spanner head made to fit a nut on a particular size of Whitworth thread will also fit a nut on a BSF thread, but of a different size. Both sizes are usually marked on these spanners - see illustration.

Spanners for British Standard Pipe thread are sized in inches according to the bore of the pipe on which the thread is normally used.

British Association threads are sized by code number from 0 (6mm diameter thread) to 25 (0.25mm diameter thread). The spanners are sized using this code number followed by **BA** - eg **4BA.**

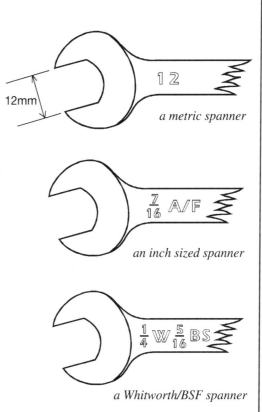

a metric spanner

an inch sized spanner

a Whitworth/BSF spanner

Hand tools - spanners

Types of spanner

Open-ended spanner

This is the general purpose spanner widely used throughout engineering. Most open-ended spanners are double-ended, the two heads on the spanner each fitting a different size of hexagon.

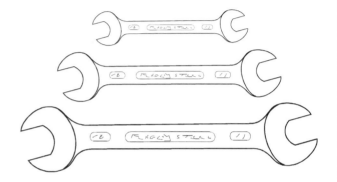

The length of the shaft of a spanner is proportional to the diameter of the thread for which it is intended - spanners for large diameter threads have longer shafts than spanners for smaller threads. For general purpose open-ended spanners the length is usually 16 times the diameter of the thread. This limits the force that can be applied to a thread and you should never add extensions to a spanner to increase the leverage.

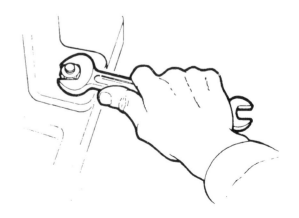

Hand tools - spanners

On an open-ended spanner the line of the jaws is at an angle to the line of the shaft - 15° is usual. This feature can be useful when using the spanner in confined spaces. The flats on a hexagon nut are at an angle of 60° to each other. By turning the spanner over and replacing it on the same pair of flats, the shaft of the spanner is repositioned by 30° - just half the angular movement achieved by moving the spanner to the adjacent pair of flats.

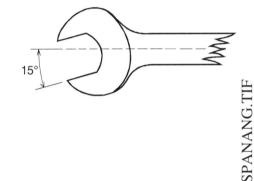

SPANANG.TIF

Do not use spanners which have damaged jaws - these can slip off the hexagon under pressure and may cause injury to you and damage to the workpiece. Check that the faces of the jaws are flat and parallel to each other.

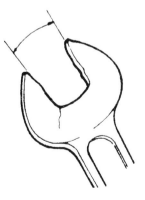

45

Ring spanners

These are gradually replacing the open-ended type
of spanner as a general purpose tool. It is easier
and more convenient to use when the swing of the
spanner is restricted. However, it will only fit nuts
and bolt heads which are in good condition. If the
corners of the hexagon are damaged it may be
necessary to use an open-ended spanner.

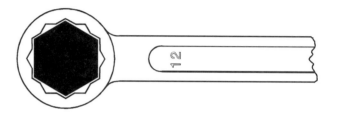

The shaft of a ring spanner may be in line with the
head, at a slight angle, or cranked as shown in the
lower illustration. Each has advantages for
particular applications.

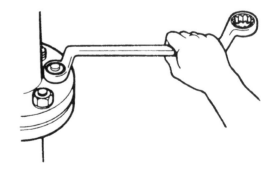

Hand tools - spanners

Combination spanner

These have an open-ended spanner at one end of the
shaft and a ring spanner at the other end. The two ends
usually fit hexagons of the same size.

Adjustable spanner

This can be used instead of an open-ended spanner or a
ring spanner. The jaws are adjustable to accommodate
various sizes of nuts and bolt heads within a certain
range.

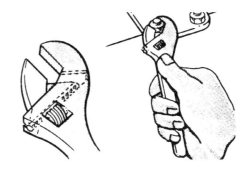

Hand tools - spanners

Box spanners

These are usually formed out of steel tube, but sometimes they are made from an alloy steel. They are useful when the nut or bolt is in a recess.

Box spanners made out of steel tube are not very strong and easily become damaged. Do not use a box spanner on which the hexagon end has become worn or rounded, or the corners have cracked or split.

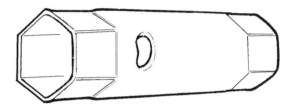

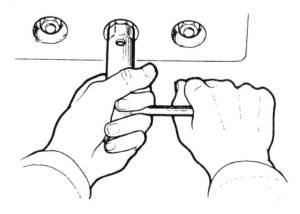

Hand tools - spanners

Socket sets

Socket sets are made up of a range of socket heads together with a selection of turning handles, extension pieces and universal joints. There is usually a handle with a ratchet which can be set to operate in either the clockwise or anticlockwise direction.

The socket heads are forged out of alloy steel.

A socket set is invaluable when the nut or bolt is located in a fairly inaccessible position. By using the appropriate socket in conjunction with various other components from the set, you can make up a spanner to suit almost any application provided that there is sufficient headroom over the hexagon to locate the socket.

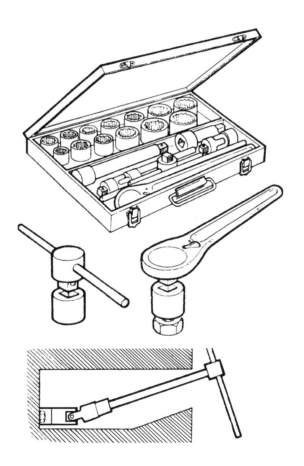

Hand tools - spanners

Hexagon socket wrenches

These are also called Allen keys. They are made from hexagonal steel bent at a right angle and are for use on hexagon socket head screws.

They are identified by their size across flats and are available in metric sizes and in inch sizes. You must always take care to use the correct size of wrench otherwise both the wrench and the screw socket will become rounded.

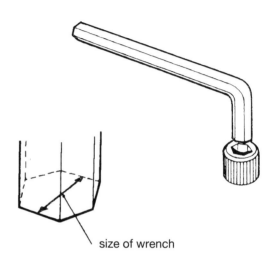

size of wrench

Do not use a hexagon socket wrench which has rounded edges - it will slip in the socket and is likely to damage the head of the screw.

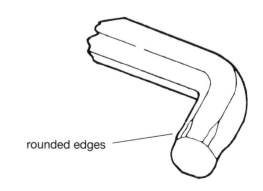

rounded edges

Hand tools - spanners

SAFETY when using spanners

Accidents with spanners are nearly all caused by the spanner slipping from the nut. Accidents can be prevented by using spanners correctly:

- use the correct size of spanner for the job

- never pack the gap with washers or other materials

- use a rigid spanner rather than an adjustable spanner - there is less chance of it slipping

- pull towards your body whenever possible

- do not extend the spanner with lengths of tube to obtain extra leverage

- use a steady pull, not a jerky action

- do not hit the spanner with a hammer

- ensure that your hands will not strike an obstruction if the nut turns unexpectedly.

Screwdrivers

Screwdrivers are made in various lengths and designs.
Screws are driven by turning the screwdriver handle
while applying a force onto the screw head.

Types of screwdriver

Engineers' screwdrivers

These are for use on slotted screws and generally have a
flared tip on the end of either a round or square section
blade. The edges of the flared tip are usually ground back
on an engineers' screwdriver - see lower illustration.
They are available with overall lengths up to 300mm and
with tip widths up to 10mm. For general purpose
engineers' screwdrivers, the wider the tip the longer the
blade. However, screwdrivers with wide tips and short
blades are available for use in restricted space and narrow
tip screwdrivers with long blades are used when a long
reach is necessary.

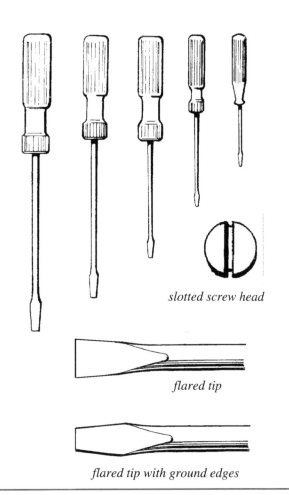

slotted screw head

flared tip

flared tip with ground edges

Hand tools - screwdrivers

Electricians' screwdrivers

These normally have round blades and may have either parallel tips or flared tips. The handle is made of an insulating plastic and the blade is often sheathed in an insulating material so that only the tip of the blade is exposed.

Sometimes there is a neon indicator inside the handle which is connected between the blade and a metal ring on the top of the handle. Live high voltage sources can be detected with safety by touching the tip of the blade on the suspected source and earthing the top of the handle through the finger - if the source is live the neon will glow.

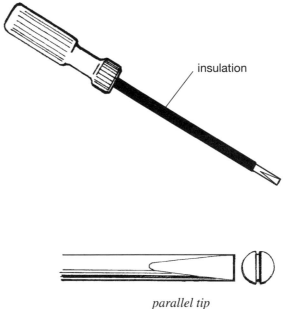

insulation

parallel tip

53

Hand tools - screwdrivers

Crosspoint screwdrivers

These are also called cruciform screwdrivers.

There are several types of crosshead screw in use - the two most common are "Phillips" and "Pozidriv". These screwdrivers are made in a range of four point sizes from No.1 to No.4 - size No.4 being the largest.

It is important that you use the correct type and size of screwdriver point for the screws in use, otherwise damage is likely to be caused to both the screw and the screwdriver point. Note that damaged crosshead screws are particularly difficult to remove.

Never try to turn a crosshead screw with a straight tip screwdriver.

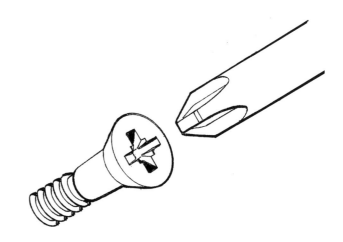

Using screwdrivers

Do not use damaged screwdrivers. A tip which is chipped or rounded will not seat properly in the screw head and is likely to damage both the screw head and the workpiece.

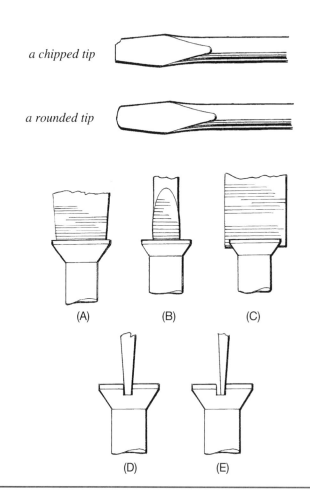

a chipped tip

a rounded tip

Choose a screwdriver which is correctly shaped and the right size to fit snugly in the screw head.

- The tip of the blade should extend across almost the full width of the slot in the screw head (A). If the tip is not wide enough (B), it will not grip the screw correctly and is likely to damage the slot. A tip which is wider than the screw head (C) will damage the surrounding area of the workpiece when the screw is driven home.

(A)   (B)   (C)

- The tip should be thin enough to enter fully into the slot of the screw head (D), but it should not be so thin that there is excessive play (E).

(D)   (E)

Hand tools - pliers

Pliers

Pliers are basically gripping tools. They are used to hold small components which would otherwise be difficult to hold and control. Pliers are made of forged or cast steel with the jaws hardened or tempered. They are sized by overall length. The more common types are described on the following pages.

Types of pliers

Flat nosed pliers

These are the basic pliers. They are used solely for gripping and holding.

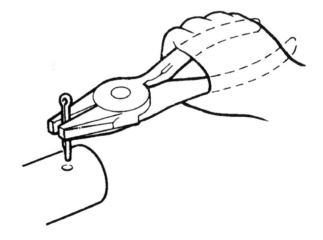

Hand tools - pliers

Combination pliers

These are more versatile tools than flat nosed pliers and have a greater number of applications. They incorporate side cutters, joint cutters and a pipe grip.

The side cutters are useful for cutting locking wire and split pins to length.

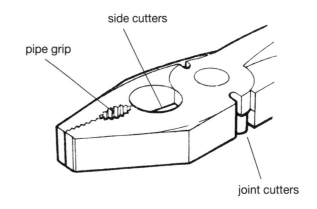

side cutters

pipe grip

joint cutters

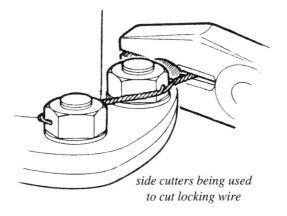

*side cutters being used
to cut locking wire*

Hand tools - pliers

Electrical pliers

These are similar to combination pliers but the handles are heavily insulated to withstand high voltages. Electrical pliers are usually tested to withstand 10,000 volts.

Snipe nosed pliers

These are more delicate pliers for holding small components.

Round nosed pliers

Mainly used for forming loops on the ends of wires.

Special purpose pliers

There are many other plier-like tools for special applications. These include circlip pliers, wire strippers, side cutters, eyelet pliers and crimping tools.

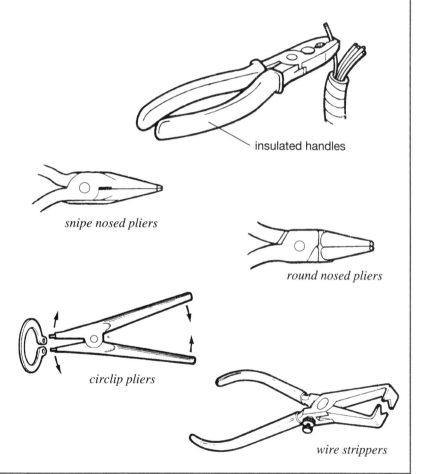

insulated handles

snipe nosed pliers

round nosed pliers

circlip pliers

wire strippers

Hand tools - pliers

Care and use of pliers

Pliers should be examined periodically for wear or damage and faulty tools discarded. The most common faults are listed below.

- Sloppy jaws which tilt relative to each other - caused by a worn pivot.

- Worn or damaged serrations prevent proper gripping.

- Sprung jaws which prevent the faces of the jaws closing together over the full length.

- Indentations or chips on the edges of the side cutters.

A finished surface should be protected when gripping with pliers to avoid the finish being damaged by the jaw serrations.

NEVER use pliers to undo or tighten nuts or bolts - pliers will cause considerable damage to the hexagon head by rounding the corners.

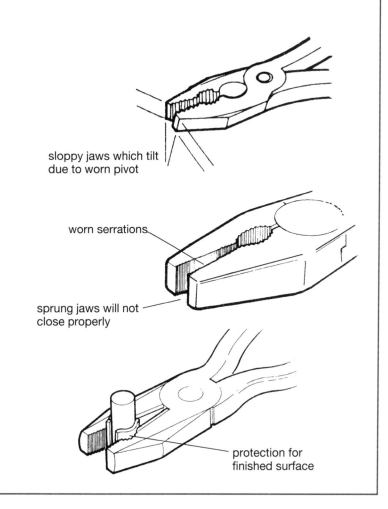

sloppy jaws which tilt due to worn pivot

worn serrations

sprung jaws will not close properly

protection for finished surface

Wrenches

A wrench is used for gripping and turning pipes and similar
objects. The grip of a wrench tightens as force is applied to bring
about rotation. Wrenches have deeply serrated jaws which bite
into the workpiece - they should not be used on surfaces where
marking is unacceptable.

Types of wrench

Pipe wrench

A pipe wrench consists of two pieces held together with a pivot
pin secured by a nut. The piece with the lower jaw is a tight **U**
shape in section and enfolds the stem of the upper jaw. The pivot
pin can be put into any one of a number of holes on the inner piece
of the wrench (see dashed outlines on illustration) and this enables
the distance between the jaws to be varied for gripping different
sizes of pipe.

This pattern of pipe wrench is capable of gripping and turning
pipes up to about 50mm bore but the amount of leverage for
turning pipes of this size is limited.

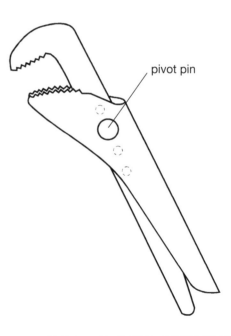

pivot pin

Hand tools - wrenches

Stillson wrench

These are made from drop forged steel with special treatment to the jaws to make them tough and hard. The floating head principle of the design provides a great gripping force as the turning force is applied to the handle.

Stillson wrenches are made in various sizes up to 900mm overall length and are able to grip round objects of more than 100mm diameter.

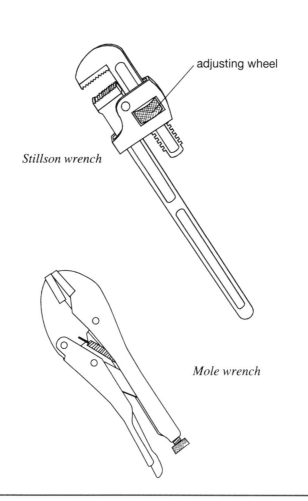

adjusting wheel

Stillson wrench

Mole wrench

Mole wrenches are made from pressed steel and cadmium plated. They have serrated jaws which can be locked onto the workpiece with a fairly powerful grip. The lock is released by a quick release lever.

The wrench can be adjusted to grip different sizes of object by turning an adjusting screw.

Mole wrench

62

Drilling

Drilling is the process of making a hole using a cutting tool which rotates relative to the workpiece and advances along the axis of rotation into the workpiece. This section also covers the associated processes of counterboring, countersinking and spotfacing.

Drilling machines

There are many types of machine for drilling, from small hand powered devices to very large computer controlled machines. The bench fitter is usually only concerned with hand-held drilling devices and the bench and pillar drilling machines.

Hand-held drills

Hand-held drills are used for drilling small holes when neither the size (diameter) nor the direction of the hole is required to close tolerances.

The hand drill

The drill bit is held in a chuck connected to a pinion. This is turned by a gear wheel rotated by hand. Hand pressure on the top handle is used to keep the drill bit cutting into the workpiece.

The hand drill is suitable for drilling holes up to 8mm diameter.

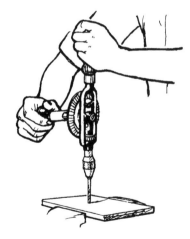

hand drill

Drilling - drilling machines

The breast drill

This is similar to the hand drill except that there is a breastplate instead of a top handle and it is usually lower geared. Pressure is applied to the drill bit by leaning onto the breastplate. The ability to apply greater pressure to the drill bit and the lower gearing make the breast drill suitable for drilling larger holes.

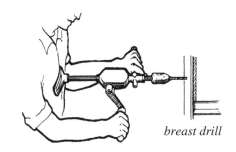
breast drill

The breast drill is suitable for drilling holes up to about 13mm diameter.

Electric drills

The drill bit is rotated by an electric motor. The hands are used to apply pressure to the drill bit and stabilise the direction of drilling. The larger hand-held electric drills are suitable for drilling holes up to 13mm diameter (in metal) provided that they have an appropriate speed control.

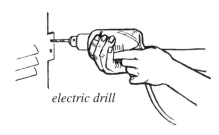
electric drill

Compressed air drills

These are sometimes called pneumatic drills. They are similar to the electric drill except that compressed air is used as the source of power.

compressed air drill

Bench drilling machine

As its name implies, this type of drilling machine is mounted on a bench. It has a limited capacity, both in the size of workpiece which can be accommodated and the diameter of hole which can be drilled.

The spindle is generally belt-driven and the speed is changed by altering the position of the drive belt on a pair of stepped pulleys. The drill is fed into the work by hand pressure on the feed handle. The pressure must be fairly gentle and the operator can feel the drill cutting. This type of handfeed is often called a "sensitive feed".

Most bench drilling machines are able to drill holes up to 13mm (½ inch) diameter.

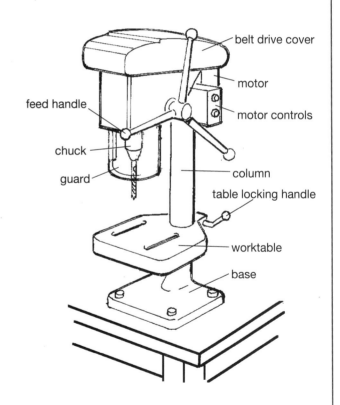

belt drive cover

motor

feed handle

motor controls

chuck

guard

column

table locking handle

worktable

base

Drilling - drilling machines

Adjusting the worktable

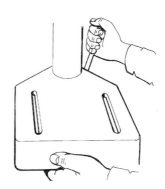

- Stand at an angle to the machine so that the locking screw can be controlled but you are still in a suitable position to support the weight of the table.

- Hold the worktable by gripping the underside at the front with one hand - be prepared to take the weight of the table.

- With the other hand slowly release the locking screw - it is sometimes necessary to tap the locking screw with the palm of the hand.

- As soon as the weight of the table is felt by the supporting hand, stop releasing the locking screw and transfer the second hand to share the load of the table.

- Swivel the table from side to side while adjusting the height.

- When the table is in the required position, again take the weight on one hand and tighten the locking screw.

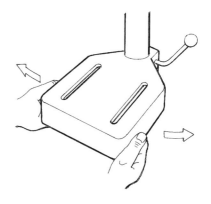

Drilling - drilling machines

Spindle speed

The speed of the machine is varied by changing the position of the belt on the stepped pulley wheels.

- A large driver pulley turning a smaller driven pulley produces a high speed.

- A small driver pulley turning a large driven pulley produces a slower speed.

Changing the spindle speed

SAFETY - always switch off the machine and ensure that it is electrically isolated before removing the drive belt cover.

- Isolate the machine from the electricity supply.

- Remove the guard covering the drive belt and pulley wheels.

- Decide whether the belt is to be raised or lowered to give the required speed and on which set of stepped pulleys the belt will change to a smaller diameter.

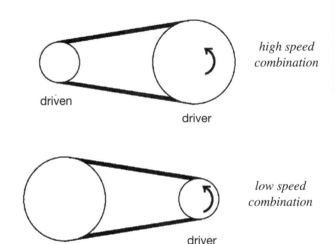

high speed combination

driven

driver

low speed combination

driver

driven

Drilling - drilling machines

- Put one hand on the belt centrally between the stepped pulleys and maintain a pull on the belt in the direction in which it has to be moved - up or down as required.

- With the other hand, turn one of the stepped pulleys so that the first hand travels towards the pulley on which the diameter is to be reduced. If sufficient force is applied, the belt will ride over the flange of the pulley into the next smaller diameter and the belt will become slack.

- Using the slackness in the belt, position the belt into the required step of the pulley on which the diameter is to be reduced.

- Position one side of the belt in the appropriate step of the second pulley and turn the pulley so that the belt is pulled onto the pulley over the flange - it may require quite a lot of force to pull the belt right round the second pulley.

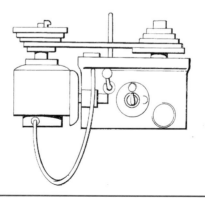

- Check that the belt is running in line on the correct steps, then replace the guard cover.

NOTE: it is important that the belt runs in line and is at the correct tension - if in doubt consult your supervisor or instructor.

Drilling - drilling machines

Depth stop mechanism

Attached to the sliding spindle support on the drilling machine is a depth stop mechanism. This stops the movement of the spindle, and therefore the depth of drilling, at a predetermined point. This is particularly useful for repetitive work.

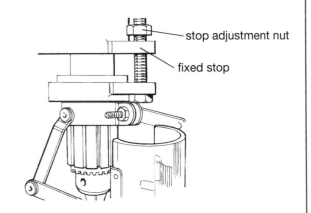

stop adjustment nut

fixed stop

Using the depth stop mechanism.

- With the drill in the chuck and the spindle not revolving, bring the drill point gently into contact with the work surface and hold in that position.

- Set the stop adjustment nut a distance above the fixed stop equal to the depth of hole required.

- Tighten the lock nut against the stop adjustment nut.

- Raise the drill off the workpiece and check that the guard is in the correct position.

- Start the spindle revolving and drill in the normal manner until the depth stop prevents further downward movement of the spindle.

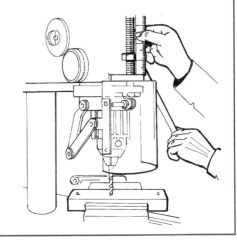

Pillar (or pedestal) drilling machine

This type of drilling machine can range from a belt-driven handfed machine, effectively a bench drilling machine with an extended column for floor mounting, to the much heavier and more versatile machine illustrated.

In the machine illustrated, the spindle is driven by the motor through a gear box. The spindle speed is changed by selecting different gears using levers.

The spindle can be fed by hand, which is useful for drilling small holes and for work setting, but there is also an adjustable power driven feed, which is desirable when drilling large diameter holes.

The worktable is moved up and down the column by a crank handle which operates a rack and pinion mechanism. This is necessary on larger drilling machines as the worktable is too heavy to be supported in the hand.

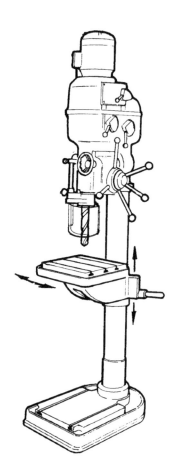

Drilling - twist drills

Twist drills

Although there are other types of drill, such as straight flute drills and flat drills, these are not often encountered in the modern engineering environment. This book therefore deals only with twist drills.

Twist drills can be made of different grades of steel, but by far the most common is high speed steel. The material from which the drill is made is usually engraved on the neck of the shank - high speed steel drills are marked HSS.

A twist drill has:

- a shank which is used to hold the drill in the drilling machine

- a body which gives the drill "reach" and determines the maximum depth of hole which can be drilled

- a tip or point which cuts the hole.

Some drills, usually the larger sizes, have a neck (see illustration).

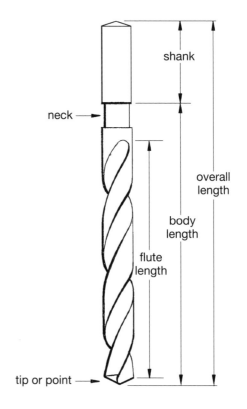

Drilling - twist drills

The drill shank

There are many different types of drill mounting for special applications but the two types in general use are the parallel shank and the Morse taper shank.

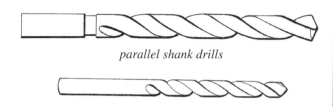

parallel shank drills

Parallel shank drills

These are the most common drills, particularly for small diameters. They can be used in drilling machines, hand-held drills and machine tools.

Parallel shank drills are held in a chuck. A three jaw self-centring chuck is usual and each chuck will hold the full range of drill sizes up to its maximum capacity.

The shank of a parallel drill must be clean and in good condition if the drill is to revolve accurately. Do not let the shank of a drill turn inside the jaws of the chuck, otherwise the shank will become scored and this will affect the true running of the drill.

self-centring drill chuck

Drilling - twist drills

Taper shank drills

These are available in all but the smallest diameters of drill. They give a more positive drive and are useful when quick changing is desirable. Note that the tang on the end of the taper does NOT drive the drill - it is there so that the drill can be extracted from the machine spindle using a tapered drift (see later).

The tapered shank is a standard Morse taper. There are eight sizes of Morse taper from size 0 (the smallest) through to size 7. A range of drill diameters is covered by each Morse taper size.

Each drilling machine will have a particular size of Morse taper socket in the end of its spindle. Drills with this size of taper can be fitted direct to the spindle. Drills with different sized tapers can be fitted using an adaptor sleeve or socket.

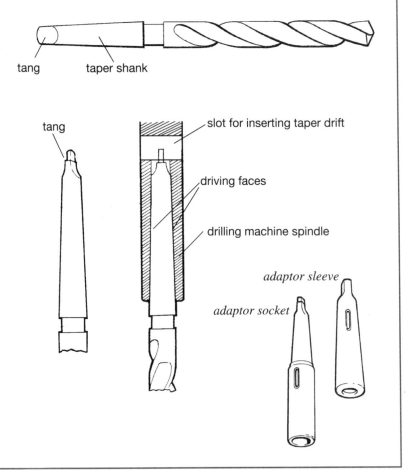

tang   taper shank

tang

slot for inserting taper drift

driving faces

drilling machine spindle

adaptor sleeve

adaptor socket

Drilling - twist drills

The drill body

The flutes

The body of a twist drill has spiral grooves in it called flutes. These allow swarf to flow out of the hole being drilled. Most twist drills have two flutes.

There are drills which have three flutes and others with four flutes. These are mainly used for enlarging existing holes, for example in cored castings. A two flute drill used for this purpose would chatter and give oversize or oval holes. A three or four flute drill can also be used to correct the alignment of an existing hole or to improve the finish.

There are drills which have different angles of spiral (or helix). The standard helix angle is about 30° and this is used for general purpose drilling. A slow spiral drill is used for drilling hard crumbly materials such as brass, bronze, magnesium, mica and perspex. For soft materials which form long stringy chips, such as aluminium, aluminium alloys and wood, a quick spiral drill will give better results.

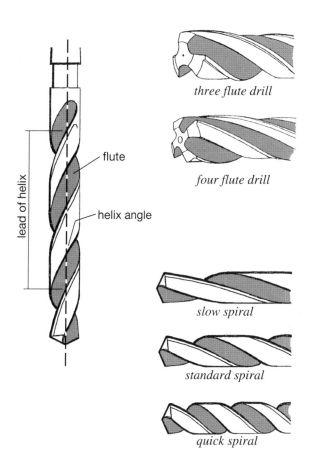

lead of helix

flute

helix angle

three flute drill

four flute drill

slow spiral

standard spiral

quick spiral

Drilling - twist drills

The lands

The body of a twist drill is reduced below the nominal size of the drill apart from a thin continuous strip along the lower edge of each flute. These strips are called the lands.

When drilling, only the lands are in contact with the sides of the hole. The lands run right down to the drill point and form part of the cutting edge. It is the distance across the lands that determines the size of hole that the drill will make. In the section drawing, the broken line shows the size of hole.

The web

The narrowest part of the body is in the centre - this is called the web. A thick web makes the drill strong and rigid, but a thin web is desirable at the drill point so that the chisel edge is kept short. Therefore the web is usually tapered; it is quite thin near the drill point and gets thicker towards the shank.

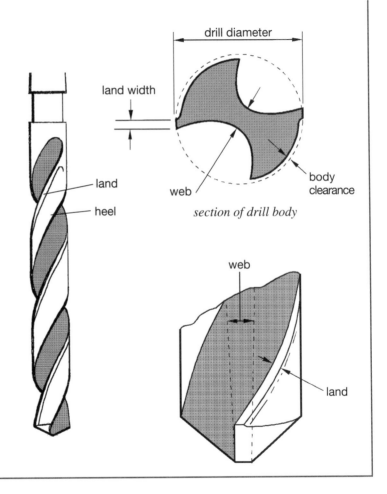

section of drill body

The drill point

The drill point is the whole of the conical end of the drill. It is this which cuts the hole. The most important elements of the drill point are:

- the point angle

- the chisel edge angle

- the lip clearance angle.

These angles are discussed on the following pages.

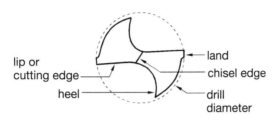

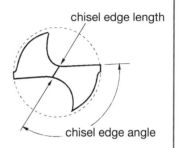

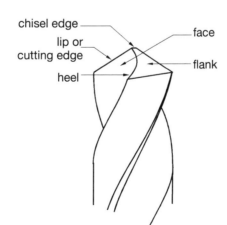

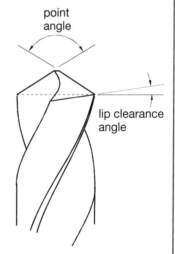

Drilling - twist drills

Point angle

The standard point angle is 118°. The shape of the flutes of a standard twist drill is such that when the point is ground to this angle the cutting edge is a straight line.

More acute (sharper) point angles, down to 60°, are useful when drilling brittle plastics and other materials which have a tendency to flake away on the under face as the drill breaks through.

Drills with a flatter angle are called obtuse points. Angles as large as 140° are advantageous on the harder steels and those which tend to work-harden. A flat point (180°) is used for drilling flat-bottomed holes. Note that a standard drill ground to an obtuse angle has a concave cutting edge - this results in weakened outer corners.

It is important that the point angle is symmetrical about the axis of the drill so that the two lips are both at the same angle to the axis (59° in the case of a standard point angle) and of equal length. If the lips are of different lengths or at different angles, the drill will produce an oversize hole.

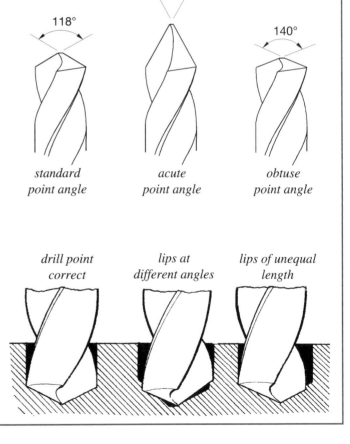

standard point angle *acute point angle* *obtuse point angle*

drill point correct *lips at different angles* *lips of unequal length*

Drilling - twist drills

Chisel edge angle

The chisel edge angle is the angle between the line of the chisel edge and line of the lip (cutting edge). It should be between 125° and 130°.

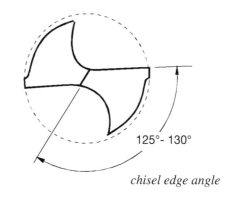

chisel edge angle

Lip clearance angle

For most purposes an angle between 10° and 12° is ideal.

Drills ground with an acute point angle for drilling brittle materials often have a larger lip clearance angle of about 20°. Obtuse angle drill points for use on hard steels generally have a smaller lip clearance angle of 6° to 8°.

An over large lip clearance angle reduces the support behind the cutting edge. Although there will be an initial free cutting action, the ultimate result will be oversize holes and reduced tool life.

Insufficient clearance will result in rubbing behind the cutting edge. This will generate heat, require more power and lead to poor holes and drill breakage.

Note that if there is no lip clearance angle the drill will not cut at all.

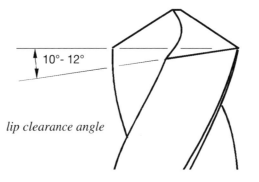

lip clearance angle

Drilling - twist drills

Self-centring drill points

The flat chisel edge of a standard twist drill has a
tendency to wander from the desired position as the
drilling operation is started. Several modifications to
the standard drill geometry have been developed to
try to overcome this problem by curving the chisel
edge or grinding it away to leave a true point. These
techniques do result in a self-centring action but
weaken the drill point or reduce the effectiveness of
the cutting action.

Sharpening drill points

Twist drills can be sharpened by hand on a pedestal
grinder, but this requires a great deal of care and skill.

Ideally, drills should be sharpened on a special drill
sharpening machine which enables all the required
angles to be generated accurately and consistently.

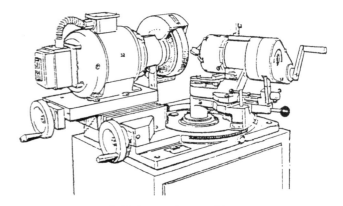

a drill sharpening machine

Drilling - twist drills

Drill sizes

Parallel shank drills are generally available in diameters from 0.2mm to 15mm and taper shank drills from 3mm to 100mm or more. On drills which have a neck, the diameter is usually engraved on the neck. The smaller size drills with parallel shanks have the diameter marked on the shank.

When the size marking on the drill is not legible a drill gauge can be used to identify the diameter. The drill is tried in progressively larger holes until you find the hole into which it will just fit. The diameter can then be read from the markings on the gauge.

Short drills are stronger and more rigid than longer drills. A short drill will therefore produce a more accurate hole and be less likely to break than a longer drill of the same diameter. However, a long drill must be used when a deep hole is required or a long reach is necessary.

Parallel shank drills up to 12mm (½inch) diameter are made in three different lengths for each diameter:

- stub drills, which are short

- jobbers drills, of medium length (these are the most common)

- long series drills, used only when the extra length is necessary.

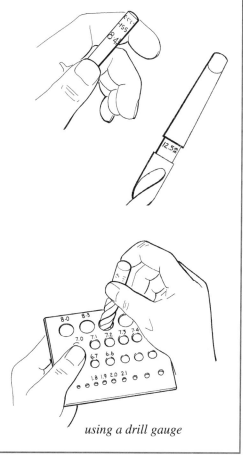

using a drill gauge

Drilling - twist drills

Mounting drills

SAFETY

Great care must be taken when mounting drills or using drilling
machines.

- The chuck key must always be removed and all guards in place
  before the machine is started.

- There must be no loose clothing or long hair which could get
  caught up in the drill.

- It is sensible to wear protective gloves when handling drills as
  they can become very hot in use. Gloves will also prevent your
  hands from getting cut by swarf which may be on the drill.

Mounting parallel shank drills

Parallel shank drills should only be mounted in a drill chuck.

- Select the required size of drill.

- Check that it is straight, that the drill point is not worn or chipped
  and that the shank is not scored.

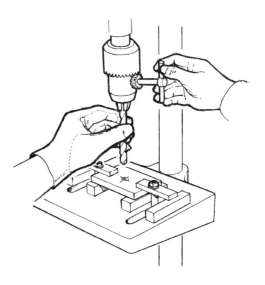

Drilling - twist drills

- Clean the drill including the shank.

- Open out the drill chuck until the drill shank will slide up between the chuck jaws.

- Hold the drill centrally in position between the jaws with the minimum necessary amount of the shank protruding and tighten the chuck using the chuck key.

- Ensure that the drill is held securely.

- Check that the chuck key has been removed and that the guards are in position.

- Start the drilling machine and check that the drill is running true.

- If the drill is out of true stop the machine, remove the drill and check that the shank and the chuck jaws are clean and undamaged. Remount the drill. If it still runs out of true, discard the drill and use another.

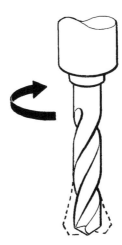

Drilling - twist drills

Mounting taper shank drills

Taper shank drills are not mounted in a chuck. The spindle of the drilling machine has an internal taper which will take the shank of the drill direct if they are both the same size. If they are of different sizes an adaptor is used. Use an adaptor sleeve if the drill shank is smaller than the spindle bore or an adaptor socket if the drill shank is larger than the spindle bore.

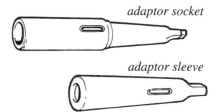

adaptor socket

adaptor sleeve

- Select the required size of drill and any necessary adaptor sleeve or socket.

- Check and clean the drill (as for parallel shank drills) and the machine spindle socket.

- If an adaptor is necessary, examine and clean the adaptor and fit it on the taper of the drill.

- Insert the drill (with adaptor if fitted) into the spindle taper of the machine and turn it until you feel the tang locate in the slot.

- Press the drill into position by tapping the end with a hide mallet or lowering the spindle so that the drill presses onto a wooden block - see illustration.

- Observe all the safety precautions on page 82, then start the machine and check that the drill is running true.

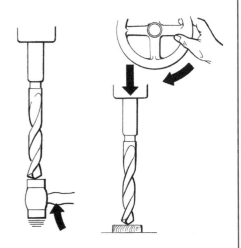

Drilling - twist drills

Demounting taper shank drills

- Place a block of wood or some other suitable soft material on the machine table under the drill.

- Insert a taper drift in the spindle nose slot. It is important that a proper mild steel taper drift is used to avoid damaging either the machine spindle or the drill.

- Support the drill with a gloved hand and strike the end of the taper drift with a hammer or mallet.

- Remove any adaptor from the drill using a similar technique with the draft.

- Clean the drill and any adaptor and return to proper storage.

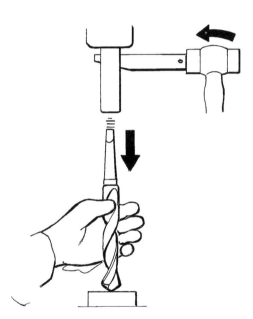

Work holding

When using a drilling machine it is important that the workpiece is held securely. There are two reasons why this is necessary.

- **For your safety** - if the workpiece is not held securely it may break free and revolve at high speed with the drill. This is particularly likely as the drill breaks through on the underside of the workpiece.

- **To drill holes accurately** - if the workpiece moves while it is being drilled the hole may be in the wrong position, oversize or oval, or even at a slight angle if the drill bends. Worst of all, the drill might break off in the workpiece and result in it being scrapped.

Small regular shaped workpieces can be held in a machine vice clamped to the worktable of the drilling machine. Large or irregular shaped workpieces are often clamped direct to the worktable.

If a number of identical workpieces are to be drilled it will probably be advantageous to set up stops on the worktable for quick and accurate location. If a large number of identical workpieces are to be drilled they may be held on the worktable using a custom made jig.

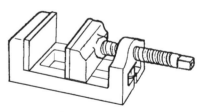

a simple machine vice

Drilling - work holding

Work holding with a machine vice

A machine vice can be bolted onto the worktable of the drilling machine by using T-bolts located in the worktable slots. When mounting the vice ensure that the table (including the slots) and the base of the vice are clean and free from burrs.

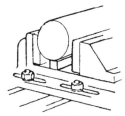

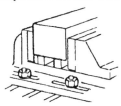

parallel strips used to raise workpiece

- Position the maximum possible length and depth of the workpiece in the vice. If holding a cylindrical workpiece ensure that the centre line is lower than the top of the vice jaws.

- If it is necessary to raise the height of the workpiece in the vice jaws, use parallel strips. Check that the strips will not foul the drill during the drilling operation.

- Close the vice jaws lightly onto the workpiece.

- Tap the workpiece down in the jaws using a soft hammer. If the workpiece is not seated it will ring as it is struck, the sound changing to a dull thud as the workpiece seats on the vice bed or the parallel strips.

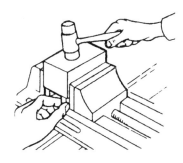

- Use a feeler gauge to check that the workpiece is fully seated. If parallel strips have been used, check that they are tightly trapped.

- Fully tighten the vice.

Drilling - work holding

Clamping flat work in a machine vice

- Clamp the vice to the drilling machine worktable. Use T-slot bolts, nuts and washers. Always use washers to prevent the clamping nuts biting into the vice.

- Select a pair of parallels and position them between the jaws of the vice - see illustration. Make sure that the parallels are a matched pair.

- Place the workpiece in-between the vice jaws and on top of the parallels. Lightly tighten the vice jaws.

- Check that the parallels are positioned clear of the area of drilling.

- Lightly tap the work with a soft hammer to bed it down onto the parallels.

- Tighten the vice jaws onto the work using the palm of the hand to tap the handle. Do not use a hammer to tighten the vice - this would be likely to strain the vice and damage the screw.

- Check that the parallels are tightly trapped.

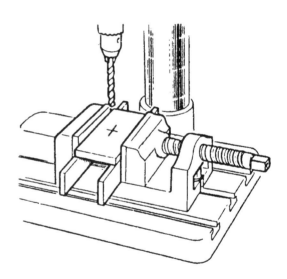

Drilling - work holding

Clamping flat work

- Ensure that the drill table is free from swarf and dirt.

- Select a matched pair of parallels and place them on the drill table.

- Place the work on top of the parallels so that the position of the required hole is in line with the drill spindle.

- Position the parallels so that they are as close as possible to opposite edges of the work and clear of the drilling area.

- Check that the work is lying flat on the parallels.

- Position T-slot bolts and clamps on both sides of the work. The parallels should be directly below the clamps to avoid tilting the work.

- Tighten both clamps alternately and evenly.

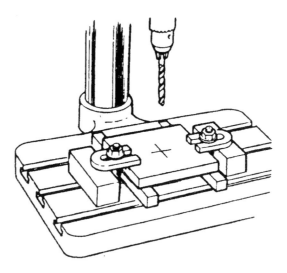

Clamping irregularly shaped workpieces

The method used to hold an irregularly shaped workpiece securely on the drill table will vary considerably depending upon the characteristics of the workpiece and how it is to be drilled. An example which illustrates some of the principles is given below.

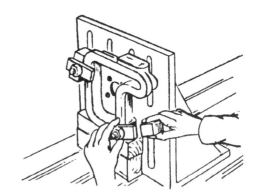

- Choose a suitable size of angle plate and secure it to the drill table using T-slot bolts.

- Preposition clamps in appropriate slots on the angle plate.

- Position the workpiece flat against the angle plate. If drilling close to the angle plate, build up the height of the workpiece with packing so that the drill chuck will not foul the top edge of the angle plate.

- Lightly tighten the clamps to hold the workpiece against the angle plate but still allow some movement.

- Place a spirit level on the face to be drilled. Tap the workpiece with a soft hammer until the surface becomes horizontal.

- Finally, tighten the clamps and check again with the spirit level to ensure that the workpiece is accurately positioned.

Drilling - work holding

Clamping round work

The best way of clamping a round bar onto the drill table is to use a vee block. Longer workpieces may require two vee blocks.

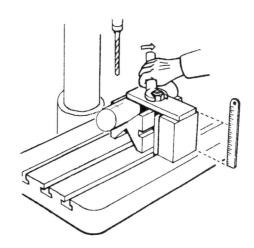

- Ensure that the drill table is free from dirt and swarf.

- Position the vee block on the table parallel with the T-slots.

- Place the workpiece on the vee block.

- Measure the height from the drill table to the top of the work and select a similar height of packing for the clamp.

- Put a strap clamp across the workpiece and packing and hold it loosely in position with the T-slot bolt.

- Rotate the workpiece in the vee block to bring the marked out position of the required hole to top dead centre.

- Tighten the strap clamp taking care that the workpiece does not move out of position.

Note: When selecting a vee block, choose a size which will allow the workpiece to rest approximately midway on the faces of the groove - see illustration. If using two vee blocks to support a workpiece, ensure that they are a matched pair.

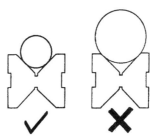

The use of stops

If several identical workpieces are to be drilled, stops can be used to locate them quickly in the same position on the drill table.

To set the stops, position them to the sides and/or the end of the workpiece to control location in the required planes. The illustrations show some typical applications of stops.

Arrange the stops so that only a small area is in contact with the workpiece. Use specially shaped blocks or turn a rectangular block slightly so that the workpiece locates on a corner.

When using stops, make sure that they locate on parts of the workpiece which can serve as datum points for the position of the holes to be drilled. Ensure that the stops and the workpiece where it comes into contact with the stops are clean and free from burrs.

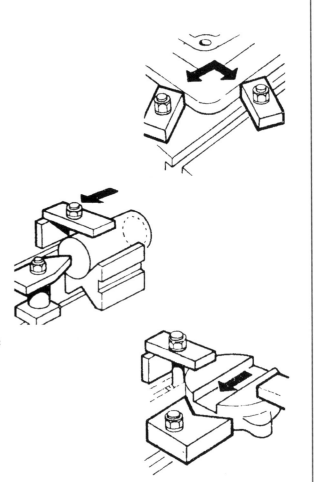

Drilling - work holding

Jigs

When a large number of identical workpieces need to be drilled a jig may be available. A jig is a device which is specially designed to hold a particular workpiece. It enables each succeeding workpiece to be located quickly and accurately in the same position so that the operation to be carried out is done in the same way and in exactly the same place on all of them.

The drilling jig is carefully secured to the drilling table and thereafter the individual workpieces can be locked accurately into position very quickly and easily.

A jig is made to a high standard of accuracy and must be able to withstand considerable wear. It is a precision tool and needs proper care. It should be kept clean and workpieces must never be forced into it. When not in use it should be stored carefully.

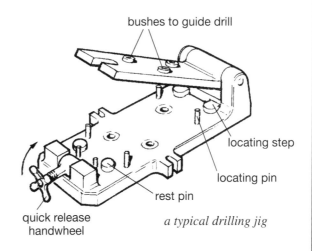

bushes to guide drill

locating step

locating pin

rest pin

quick release handwheel

a typical drilling jig

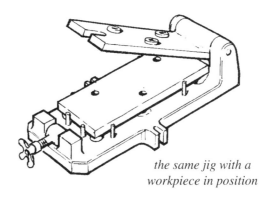

the same jig with a workpiece in position

93

Drilling - using drills

Using drills

Power driven drilling machines are dangerous.

The spindle of the machine or the drill itself can catch hold of loose hair or clothing which then quickly become entangled. This can result in severe injury.

The drill can also "snatch" at the workpiece which may break loose if inadequately secured and suddenly revolve at high speed. This is particularly likely when drilling thin workpieces and as the drill breaks through.

SAFETY

- The workpiece must always be properly secured.

- There must be adequate support for the breakthrough.

- Particular care must be taken when drilling sheetmetal.

- The drill guard must always be in position when the drill is rotating.

- Take care that your hair or clothing cannot get caught up in the rotating drill. Long hair should be covered and loose clothing avoided if possible.

Drilling - using drills

The centres of holes should be accurately marked out and centre punched. For larger drill sizes it will be necessary to centre drill or pilot drill before finally drilling to size.

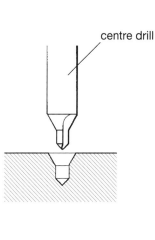

centre drill

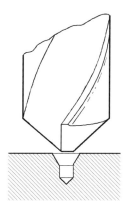

Centre drilling provides an enlarged centre to accommodate the longer chisel edge of larger diameter drills.

Pilot drilling is pre-drilling with a smaller size drill than the size of hole finally required. This provides clearance for the centre of the main drill, which enables it to cut much more efficiently.

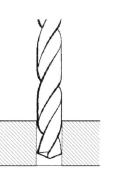

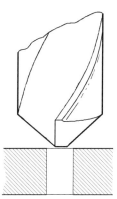

Drilling - using drills

The position of the hole should be checked before the drill has cut to the full diameter. If the hole is off centre the error can be corrected by chipping a groove back towards the true centre. This will allow the drill to restart the hole in its correct position.

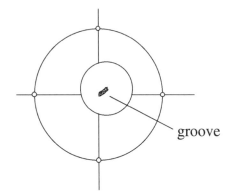

groove

Care should be taken to avoid a drill breaking in the workpiece. Broken drills are difficult to remove and often result in the work having to be scrapped. To minimise the risk of a drill breaking:

- it should always be used at the correct speed and feed

- swarf should not be allowed to clog the hole or the flutes of the drill

- suitable coolants should be used.

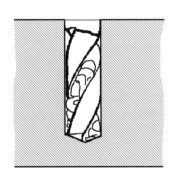

Drilling - using drills

Cutting fluids (coolants)

The major function of a cutting fluid is to keep the drill cool and thereby prevent it losing its temper through overheating. The most efficient fluid for removing heat is water because of its high heat capacity, so water-based emulsions are widely used as coolants. These emulsions inhibit rusting which would be a problem if plain water was used.

Cutting fluids also provide lubrication between rubbing parts of the drill and the workpiece. In addition, the flow of fluid helps to remove swarf from the work area.

General purpose emulsions (often incorrectly called "soluble oils") can be used for most drilling applications, but not on magnesium and certain alloys which would become stained.

It is important that the emulsion is made up in accordance with the manufacturer's instructions and that it is maintained in good condition. Swarf should be removed regularly otherwise it could cause the breakdown of the emulsion.

For more severe drilling applications at low or moderate cutting speeds, such as on tool steel or stainless steel, emulsions fortified by fatty oils or chlorine or sulphur additives give better performance. Consult manufacturers' data sheets for further information.

Cutting speed

For efficient drilling it is important to use the correct cutting speed.

The cutting speed of a drill, sometimes just called the speed, is the speed at which a point on the circumference (the outside edge) of the drill travels relative to the workpiece. It is measured in metres per minute (m/min). The spindle speed of the drilling machine, the cutting speed and the drill diameter are related by the following formula:

$$N = \frac{1000S}{\pi D}$$

where: N = spindle speed (rpm)
           S = cutting speed (m/min)
           D = drill diameter (mm)

This formula can be used to calculate the relationship between spindle speed and cutting speed for different diameters of drill. However, in the workshop it is quicker and easier to use a drill speed conversion chart. A section of a typical chart is shown alongside.

Spindle speeds in RPM				
Metres/min	3	12	30	45
mm/size	revolutions per minute			
1.0	970	3878	9695	14542
1.5	647	2589	6474	9711
2.0	485	1941	4853	7280
2.5	388	1552	3882	5823
3.0	323	1294	3234	4851
3.5	277	1108	2772	4158
4.0	243	970	2425	3638
5.0	194	776	1941	2911
6.0	162	647	1617	2426
7.0	139	554	1386	2079
8.0	121	485	1213	1819
9.0	108	431	1078	1617
10.0	97	388	970	1455
11.0	88	353	882	1323
12.0	81	323	809	1213
14.0	69	277	693	1039
16.0	61	243	607	910
18.0	54	216	539	808
20.0	49	194	485	728

Example: a 9.0mm diameter drill cutting at 12 metres/minute would run at 431rpm

Drilling - using drills

The cutting speed to be used will depend upon the properties of the material being drilled and the type of material from which the drill is made. Optimum cutting speeds are obtained from drill manufacturers' charts and booklets. These are, however, the ideal speeds and in practice it may be necessary to reduce them.

On any particular machine it may not be possible to select exactly the recommended speed, in which case the nearest lower speed should be used. Always use a lower speed rather than a higher speed to avoid overheating and damaging the drill.

Typical optimum cutting speeds for HSS (high speed steel) twist drills are shown in the table.

Typical cutting speeds or HSS twist drills

Material being drilled	Cutting speed (m/min)
Aluminium	70 - 100
Brass	35 - 50
Bronze (phosphor)	20 - 35
Cast iron (grey)	25 - 40
Copper	35 - 45
Steel (mild)	30 - 40
Steel (medium carbon)	20 - 30
Steel (alloy-high tensile)	5 - 8
Thermo-setting plastic	20 - 30

Drilling - using drills

Drill feed

The feed of the drill is the rate at which it penetrates into the workpiece. It is usually expressed as millimetres per revolution (mm/rev).

The optimum feed rate will depend upon the material from which the drill is made, the properties of the material being drilled and the diameter of the drill. Some typical feed rates for HSS twist drills when drilling low carbon steel are shown in the table.

Lower feed rates would be necessary when drilling tougher materials, such as alloy steels, but higher feed rates can be used when drilling less tough materials.

Typical feeds for HSS twist drills when drilling mild steel

Drill diameter (mm)	Rate of feed (mm.rev)
1.0 - 2.5	0.040 - 0.060
2.5 - 4.5	0.050 - 0.100
4.5 - 6.0	0.075 - 0.150
6.0 - 9.0	0.100 - 0.200
9.0 - 12.0	0.150 - 0.250
12.0 - 15.0	0.200 - 0.300
15.0 - 18.0	0.230 - 0.330
18.0 - 21.0	0.260 - 0.360
21.0 - 25.0	0.280 - 0.380

Drilling - using drills

With simple drilling machines the rate of feed is determined by the pressure applied to the feed handle by the operator. This is called "sensitive feed" drilling. Small diameter drills require only a light pressure to achieve the correct feed rate. Large drills require more pressure.

Accurate control of feed rate is necessary for good efficient drilling and when using sensitive feed this requires skill and experience in the operator.

More sophisticated drilling machines provide a power feed to the drill which can be accurately regulated to give the required rate of feed.

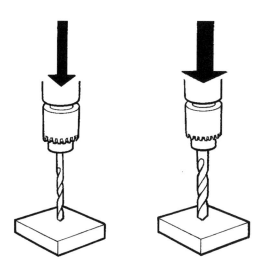

Relieving the drill

On a drilling machine where the feed is manually regulated, the pressure on the drill feed handle should be relieved momentarily at intervals. This stops the drill cutting and prevents long lengths of swarf forming. Long swarf rotating with the drill is a safety hazard and it also restricts the operator's view of the work.

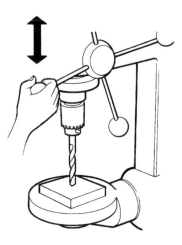

Breaking through

With experience, a drilling machine operator will be able to feel through the feed handle when the metal is becoming thin towards the end of the drilling and just before break through. When this is detected, the feed pressure should be eased off the drill. This will help it to cut cleanly on the break through with little or no burring.

Drilling - using drills

Signs of good drilling

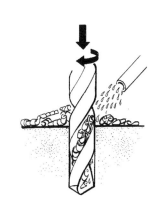

- The swarf is broken into small even sections which travel up the drill flutes with ease and emerge equally from both flutes.

- The sound is a continuous note accompanied by a spitting sound made by the chips (swarf).

- There is no discolouration of the swarf.

Signs of poor drilling

- The swarf is long and stringy, jamming in the flutes and roughening the wall of the hole.

- OR the swarf is fine and needle-shaped with chatter marks showing on the bottom of the hole.

- The sound is a vibrating whine.

- The swarf is discoloured and/or smoke rises from the drilling area.

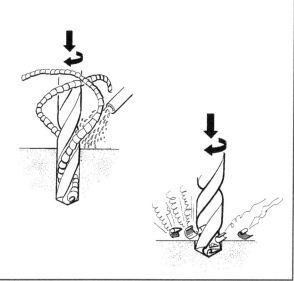

Some drilling problems

Oversize hole - could be caused by:
- lips of unequal length
- chisel edge not central
- machine spindle not running true.

Unequal chips - could be caused by:
- lips of unequal length
- lips incorrectly ground so that the chisel edge runs eccentric to the drill axis
- too great a difference in relative lip height.

Splitting up the web - could be caused by:
- insufficient lip clearance
- feed rate too high
- striking the drill point with a hard object
- ejecting the drill onto the machine base
- surface cracks on the flanks of the point caused by bad point grinding.

Broken tang
The tang of the drill is for ejection purposes only. If torque is taken by the tank it can result in breakage. Always ensure that the taper socket is free from foreign matter and damage so that the drill is driven solely by friction on the taper of the shank.

split web

Drilling - using drills

Breaking down of outer corners - could be caused by:
- peripheral speed too high
- inadequate lubrication
- interrupted feed when drilling materials which work-harden
- inadequate support for the workpiece.

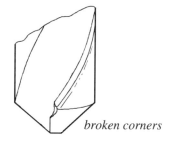
broken corners

Chipping of lips - could be caused by:
- lip clearance too great
- feed rate too high.

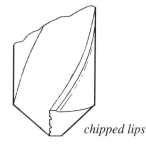
chipped lips

Breaking of drill - could be caused by:
- a worn drill
- an incorrectly ground point
- the drill slipping in the drive
- choked drill flutes
- insufficient lip clearance
- workpiece not held securely
- feed rate too high.

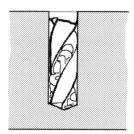

Counterboring

Counterboring is a drilling process in which an existing hole is enlarged for part of its length. The most common use for a counterbored hole is to allow the head of a bolt or screw to be sunk below the surface of the work.

Counterboring is best done with a special counterboring tool. This is basically a flat ended drill with a peg or pilot protruding from the end to locate it concentrically with the existing hole.

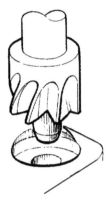

The counterboring tool can also be used for spotfacing. This is the process of levelling the area around the top of a hole to provide a flat seating at right angles to the axis of the hole. This is usually necessary for bolt holes through castings and other items with rough surfaces.

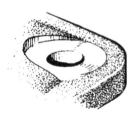

Countersinking

Countersinking is a drilling process in which a conical recess is formed concentrically at the top of an existing hole. The countersink is usually required to accommodate the head of a countersunk screw or bolt.

A special countersinking tool is used - see illustration.

The angle of a countersink is usually 45° to the axis of the hole (an included angle of 90°) but other angles may be required for special applications. The extent of the countersink is specified by stating the required outside diameter of the finished conical recess.

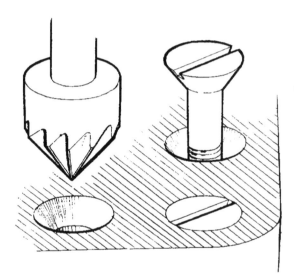

Reaming

Holes are sometimes required to have a greater degree of accuracy or a better standard of finish than can be achieved by drilling alone. In such circumstances the hole is drilled slightly smaller than required and then finished to size by reaming.

Note that reaming cannot be used to correct any inaccuracy in the position or the direction of a drilled hole.

Types of reamer

Hand reamers

Hand reamers have parallel shanks with a square on the end for fitting a wrench. This square end usually has a centre recess.

The body of a hand reamer is ground parallel but with a slight taper on the end. The taper extends for a length approximately equal to the diameter of the body. This tapered section acts as a lead into the hole to be reamed.

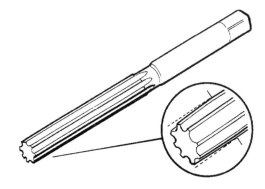

Machine reamers

Reamers made for use in power driven machines generally have Morse taper shanks, though small diameter machine reamers may have parallel shanks for holding in a chuck.

The body of a machine reamer is ground parallel with a short chamfer on the end. This chamfer forms cutting lips on the ends of the blades.

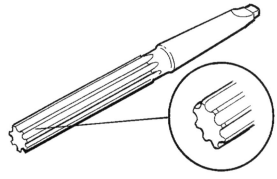

Reaming - types of reamer

Flutes

Both hand reamers and machine reamers can have either straight or spiral flutes.

straight reamer

A straight reamer will in general give the greatest accuracy and a higher standard of finish, but a spiral reamer will cut more freely and be less likely to chatter or catch if there is a slot or keyway in the hole.

spiral reamer

Note that the twist on a spiral reamer is left-handed, the opposite to that on a drill. This prevents the reamer being pulled into the hole by the rotation.

Sizes

The size of a reamer is usually engraved on the shank or the neck of the reamer together with an indication of the tolerance.

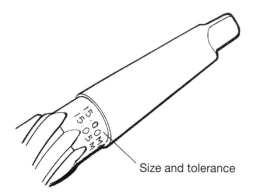

Size and tolerance

Reaming - types of reamer

Expanding reamers

Any wear along the length of the blades of a solid reamer results in inaccuracy in the reamed hole and it is not possible to reinstate the reamer to its original size. When a solid reamer is reground it has to be taken down to a slightly smaller size for which there may be no requirement.

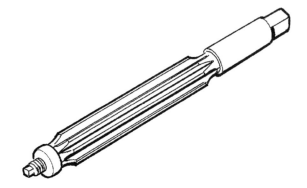

An expanding reamer has a slightly tapered bore up the centre of the body and there are slits cut between the blades. A tapered plug can be made to force the blades apart by turning a screw on the end of the body. When the blades wear they can be sprung open just enough to regrind the reamer to its original size.

This type of reamer is not intended for finishing different sizes of hole. The purpose of the expansion is solely to give a longer life to a tool for finishing standard size holes.

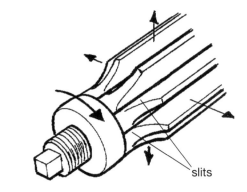

slits

Reaming - types of reamer

Adjustable reamers

Adjustable reamers have replaceable blades which fit into tapered grooves on the body. The blades slide along the grooves and can be locked into any position by tightening screwed collars. By locking the blades in different positions the reamer can be adjusted to cover quite a wide range of sizes. The adjustment is quick and accurate and infinitely variable within the range of the particular reamer.

The wide range of adjustment also allows easy compensation for wear on the blades. These can be reground and sharpened many times before replacements are needed.

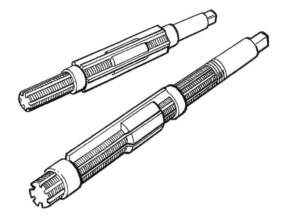

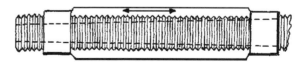

Reaming - using reamers

Using reamers

When a high degree of accuracy and finish is required, the reaming operation is best done using a hand reamer. Machine reamers are very much faster but they are not capable of giving the accuracy and finish that a skilled craftsman can achieve with a hand tool. For some work, the best approach is to machine ream the hole to within 0.1mm or less undersize and then finish with a hand reamer.

Reaming allowance

When making a reamed hole, the first step is to drill a hole which is smaller than the finished size required. The amount by which the drilled hole is undersize is called the reaming allowance.

The allowance required is different for hand reaming and machine reaming, and varies with the diameter of the hole and for different materials. It must be sufficient to allow the reamer to cut at all times. If the allowance is too small, the reamer will tend to rub in the hole and the finish and accuracy will be poor. For machine reaming mild steel, a good general rule is to leave an allowance of about 3% of the hole diameter. The allowance for hand reaming is usually a half to two-thirds of the machine reaming allowance.

Reamer manufacturers supply tables of recommended allowances for different sizes and materials.

Typical reaming allowances for machining mild steel

Diameter of hole mm	Reaming allowance mm
Up to 5	0.15 to 0.20
5 to 10	0.3
10 to 25	0.5
Over 25	0.8

Reaming - using reamers

Hand reaming

The reamer should be turned slowly and smoothly, and
excessive feed should be avoided. Observe the following
points when hand reaming.

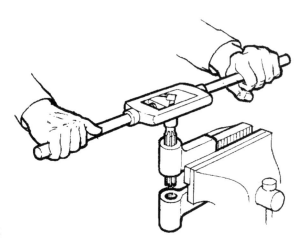

* The workpiece must be properly supported and firmly held
  in a suitable position. It is always best to have the hole
  vertical if this is possible.

* A burr on a tooth of a hand reamer will spoil the hole.
  Check carefully along the cutting edge of each tooth and if
  a burr is discovered use an oilstone to remove it.

* Use a tap wrench of appropriate size for the reamer.

* Do not attempt to start a reamer on an uneven surface. If
  you do so, as the reamer starts it will move toward the point
  of least resistance and not run true.

* Never under any circumstances should a reamer be turned
  backward (opposite to the cutting direction), even when
  removing the reamer from the workpiece.

Reaming - using reamers

Hand reaming with a drilling machine

The most accurate way to use a hand reamer is to ream each hole immediately after drilling while the work is still clamped on the table of the drilling machine. Mount a centre in the chuck of the drilling machine and use it to align and steady the reamer as it is turned by hand. Follow the reamer with the centre but do not force it. Control the feed of the reamer by hand pressure on the tap wrench. This technique will give very accurate holes but it really requires three hands - you will probably need another person to assist.

Reaming - using reamers

Machine reaming

Machine reamers are used in either a drilling machine or a lathe. When producing machine reamed holes on a drilling machine, it is customary to ream each hole immediately after drilling. This is the best way to ensure correct alignment of the reamer in the hole.

The speed of the reamer (cutting speed or spindle speed) is most important. A general guide is that the reamer can be used at up to about half the speed that is used for a drill of comparable size. In practice though, reamers are often used at much lower speeds.

The feed rate used for a reamer is generally about twice the feed rate of a drill of comparable size, but the feed should not be crowded (forced) or the reamer may tear the surface of the hole instead of cutting.

Copious quantities of a suitable cutting fluid should always be used when machine reaming. If the hole is blind, it is important to flush out chips regularly and particularly just before finishing to full depth.

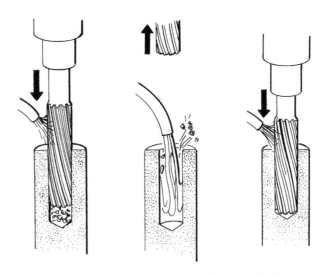

*use copious quantities of cutting fluid
and flush out the hole regularly*

117

Reaming - using reamers

Chattering

Chattering is a regular vibration in the workpiece and tool. It causes the finished hole to have a poor surface with a wave-like unevenness. Listed below are some of the more usual causes.

- Worn bearings on the machine spindle.

- Lack of rigidity in the tool or the workpiece.

- Inadequate holding of the workpiece.

- A reaming allowance which is either too large or too small.

- Insufficient or unsuitable cutting fluid.

- A blunt reamer.

- Unsuitable speed or feed.

Note that spiral reamers are less likely to chatter than straight reamers.

Signs of good cutting

- SEE that the chips are small even slithers, not round needles.

- HEAR that the sound of the cutting is a steady low pitched note, not a vibrating whine.

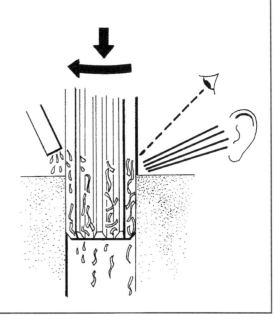

Reaming - taper reamers

Taper reamers

Taper reamers are for producing tapered holes. They are made for all standard sizes of taper and there are roughing reamers and finishing reamers. Types are available for use by hand and in machines and with either straight or spiral flutes.

To produce a tapered hole, first drill a parallel hole which has a diameter slightly smaller than the small end of the taper required. Use the roughing reamer to cut the taper into the hole and then finish with the finishing reamer.

For long tapered holes or holes which require a steep taper it is an advantage to step drill - see illustration. Careful step drilling makes the rough reaming process much faster.

Taper reaming usually requires a lot of material to be removed and this is not easily discharged from the hole. The reamer should be taken out of the hole at frequent intervals so that chips can be removed.

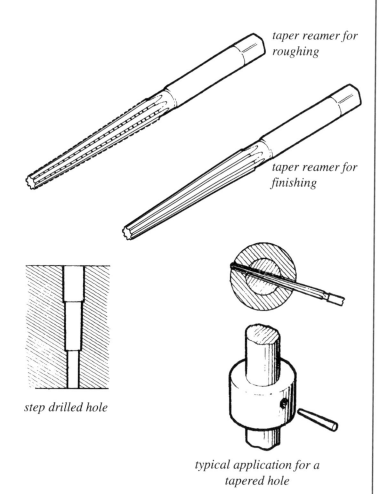

taper reamer for roughing

taper reamer for finishing

step drilled hole

typical application for a tapered hole

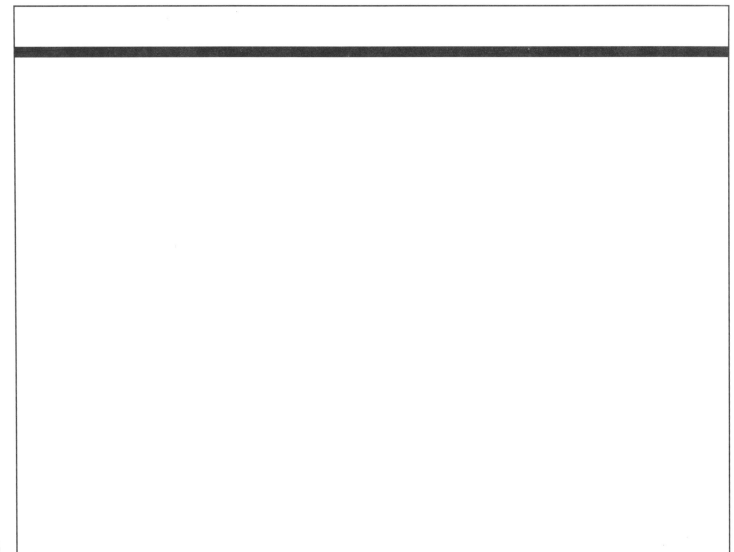

120

Screw threads

Screw threads are used widely throughout most branches of engineering. They may be used to transmit power and to increase force (as in a vehicle jack), to act as a standard for measurement (as in a micrometer) or to control movement (as does the lead screw on a lathe). However, the most common application is nuts, bolts and screws which are used to hold parts together.

Screw threads - types of thread

Types of thread

In the early days of engineering, each manufacturer produced threaded parts to his own particular ideas of the most suitable forms and dimensions. Most threaded parts were not interchangeable. Replacement of a simple bolt or nut often required complicated machining to make one which fitted.

With the passage of time, various national standards for screw threads were adopted. Each of these standards was specified for a particular range of applications. All the earlier standard threads in use in Britain were based on the imperial (inch) system of measurement. You may still come across some of these threads, but they have now largely been replaced by metric threads. Some of the more common of these earlier thread standards are listed below. The usual abbreviations are shown in brackets.

British Standard Whitworth (BSW or W)
British Standard Fine (BSF)
British Standard Pipe (BSP)
British Association (BA)
Unified Coarse (UNC)
Unified Fine (UNF)

Screw threads - types of thread

There are external and internal screw threads. Screws and bolts have external threads. Nuts and tapped holes have internal threads.

An external screw thread consists of a ridge which spirals around a circular core. An internal screw thread has a similar ridge which spirals around the inside of a hole.

Most screw threads are right-handed. When viewed end on, the ridge spirals away from you in a clockwise direction. Looking at the side of a screw, a right-handed thread slopes down towards the right.

There are also left-handed screw threads for special purposes. These are useful when a right-handed thread would tend to slacken in normal use. Left-handed screw threads also have certain safety applications. Oxygen cylinders have right-handed screw threads and acetylene cylinders have left-handed screw threads so that it is impossible to connect them the wrong way round.

Multiple-start screw threads have more than one ridge - the illustration shows a multiple-start thread with three ridges. These threads are advantageous when rapid tightening is required, but they cannot apply as much tightening force as a single-start thread.

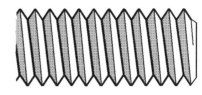

a typical screw thread (external right-handed)

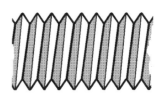

a left-handed screw thread

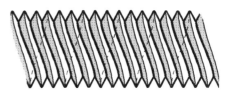

a multiple-start thread (three-start)

Screw threads - thread form

Thread form

The shape of a screw thread in section is called its form. Most screw threads are based on a symmetrical triangle and the crest and the root are usually either rounded or flattened.

The angle between the sides of the triangle that meet at the crest is called the thread angle. The thread depth is the vertical height between a crest and the adjacent root.

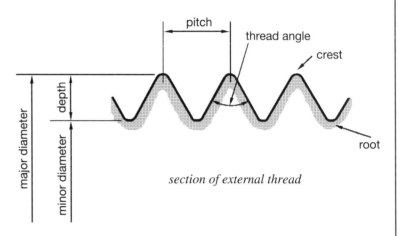

section of external thread

The major diameter of the thread is the largest dimension that can be measured over the thread. On external threads it is the largest diameter that can be measured across the thread from crest to crest. For internal threads it is the diameter measured from root to root across the bore.

The minor diameter is the smallest dimension across the screw thread. On external threads it is the diameter across the thread from root to root. For internal threads it is the distance from crest to crest across the bore.

*section of thread
with flat root and crest*

For any particular thread, both the major and minor diameters are slightly smaller on the external thread than on the internal thread. This provides a small clearance so that the threads run together easily.

Screw threads - thread form

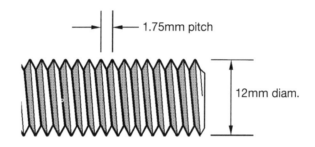

1.75mm pitch

12mm diam.

The pitch of a thread is the distance between a point on one turn of the thread to the identical point on the next turn of the thread. For example, the distance between adjacent crests or adjacent roots. On modern metric threads the pitch of the thread is stated in millimetres.

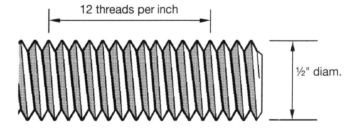

12 threads per inch

½" diam.

Screw threads specified in imperial units (inches) can have their pitch stated in decimals of an inch, but it is more usual to state the number of threads per inch. This is often abbreviated to "tpi". A British Standard Whitworth half inch (½") diameter thread has 12tpi.

Screw threads - ISO metric threads

ISO metric threads

Most threads in general use throughout Britain and Western Europe now conform to the ISO metric standards. ISO is an abbreviation for International Standards Organisation.

The ISO specifications are incorporated into British standards in BS 3643 : Part 1 : 1981 (as amended December 1984). This Standard gives full data for thread diameters from 1.0mm to 300mm.

There are coarse pitch and fine pitch metric threads. With a fine pitch thread the screw moves a shorter distance for each complete turn compared with the distance moved by a coarse pitch thread.

Fine pitch threads have a greater locking power than coarse threads and are therefore used for applications subject to vibration. However, fine pitch threads are less strong than coarse pitch threads and there is a greater danger of the thread stripping if too much force is applied. This can easily happen if the thread is in a soft metal such as aluminium.

The thread angle on all ISO metric threads is 60°. Other dimensions for a selection of coarse and fine thread sizes are given in the tables opposite.

The abbreviated description for an ISO metric thread is **M** followed by the nominal diameter and pitch. For example, a 10mm ISO metric coarse thread is written **M10 × 1.5** and a 10mm ISO metric fine thread is written **M10 × 1.25**. If the pitch is not shown, *example* **M10**, it means that the standard coarse pitch is specified.

Screw threads - ISO metric threads

ISO metric fine threads

Nominal Diameter (size) mm	Pitch mm	Major Diameter mm	Minor Diam. of Internal Threads mm
8.0	1.00	8.000	6.917
10.0	1.25	10.000	8.647
12.0	1.25	12.000	10.647
16.0	1.50	16.000	14.376
20.0	1.50	20.000	18.376
24.0	2.00	24.000	21.835

ISO metric coarse threads

Nominal Diameter (size) mm	Pitch mm	Major Diameter mm	Minor Diam. of Internal Threads mm
2.0	0.40	2.000	1.567
4.0	0.70	4.000	3.242
6.0	1.00	6.000	4.917
10.0	1.50	10.000	8.376
12.0	1.75	12.000	10.106
16.0	2.00	16.000	13.835
20.0	2.50	20.000	17.294
24.0	3.00	24.000	20.752

Tapping

A tap is a cutting tool used for making internal screw threads. It is made of hardened steel and has flutes along its body to form cutting edges. Taps intended to be used by hand have a square formed on the end of the shank to fit into a tap wrench.

Taps are available for each size of all the different standard thread forms. There are also ranges of taps available for cutting left-hand threads.

Care must be taken to keep taps in good condition. They are very brittle and easily damaged. After use a tap should be cleaned carefully and put into a suitable rack for storage.

Before using a tap examine it carefully - a tap that is chipped should not be used.

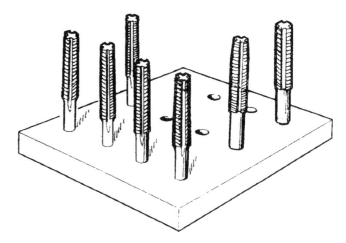

store taps in a rack to prevent the cutting edges getting damaged

Screw threads - tapping

There are three types of tap.

- **Taper tap** - this is tapered off for eight to ten threads at the leading end. It is used first and cuts gradually to the full thread size.

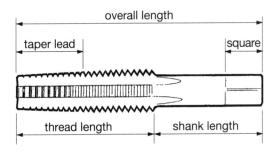

- **Intermediate tap** - this has a short chamfer extending over three or four threads at the leading end. This tap is used after the taper tap and is satisfactory for finishing open-ended holes (holes which go right through the material). The intermediate tap is sometimes called a second tap.

- **Plug tap** - this has a full-size thread right to the leading end. It is necessary to use a plug tap to cut a screw thread to the bottom of a blind hole.

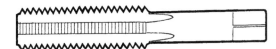

129

Screw threads - tapping

Tapping drills

To cut an internal thread it is first necessary to have a hole of the correct diameter for the particular size and form of the tap to be used. This diameter is known as the "tapping size" and a drill to make this size of hole is called a "tapping drill". You could, for example, refer to a tapping drill for an M10 × 1.50 thread.

The correct diameter of hole is approximately equal to the minor diameter of the internal thread. In fact the hole is usually very slightly larger than the minor diameter of the thread. The core diameter of a 10mm ISO metric coarse internal thread is 8.376mm and the recommended tapping size is 8.50mm.

Note that the tapping size depends not only on the nominal size of the thread but also on the thread form. A 10mm ISO metric coarse internal thread requires a different size of tapping hole to that required for a 10mm ISO metric fine internal thread. This is because the minor diameters are different even though the nominal diameters are identical. The minor diameter of the coarse thread is 8.376mm and the minor diameter of the fine thread is 8.647mm.

Manufacturers of drills and taps issue tables of recommended tapping drill sizes. This information is available as wall charts and in booklets. See the table opposite.

Screw threads - tapping

Tapping drill sizes for ISO metric coarse threads

Nominal Diameter mm	Pitch mm	Minor Diameter mm	Tapping Drill Size mm
1.0	0.25	0.729	0.75
2.0	0.40	1.567	1.60
3.0	0.50	2.459	2.50
4.0	0.70	3.242	3.30
5.0	0.80	4.134	4.20
6.0	1.00	4.917	5.00
7.0	1.00	5.917	6.00
8.0	1.25	6.647	6.80
9.0	1.25	7.647	7.80
10.0	1.50	8.376	8.50
11.0	1.50	9.376	9.50
12.0	1.75	10.106	10.20
14.0	2.00	11.835	12.00

Screw threads - tapping

Tap wrench

Hand taps are turned using a tap wrench.

A tap wrench has two handles, one on either side. The two handles enable the turning force to be applied while holding the tap in line with the hole. Never try to tap a hole using a spanner or some other single handled tool to turn the tap unless the tap is held in line by some other means.

The square end of the tap is fitted between the jaws of the tap wrench and the jaws tightened by turning the threaded handle - see illustration. Make sure that the jaws seat firmly onto the corners of the square.

Taps are brittle and easily broken. If a tap breaks off in a workpiece it is very difficult to remove and often results in the workpiece being scrapped. It is therefore important that the correct size of wrench is used for any particular tap so that it can be satisfactorily controlled.

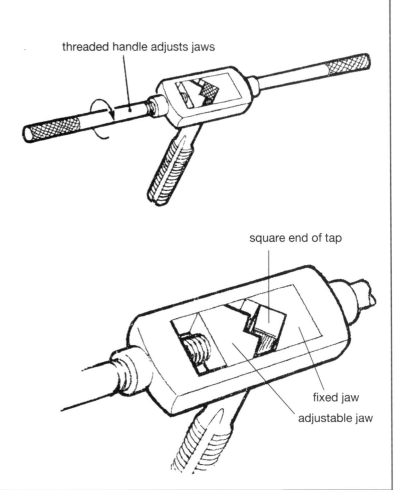

threaded handle adjusts jaws

square end of tap

fixed jaw

adjustable jaw

Screw threads - tapping

Tapping a hole

- The workpiece must be held securely.

- Start with a taper tap. Fit the tap into a tap wrench of appropriate size and insert the end of the tap into the hole which is to be threaded. If the hole is the correct tapping size the taper tap should enter by two or three threads.

- Use oil or some other suitable lubricant when threading steel or other hard materials.

- Ensure that the tap is held in line with the hole at all times - see illustration. If it is not, the hole may develop a bell mouth and the finished thread will be slack.

- Turn the tap clockwise while applying downward pressure until you can feel the tap start to cut. Once cutting has started, no further downward pressure is needed because the tap will screw itself into the hole.

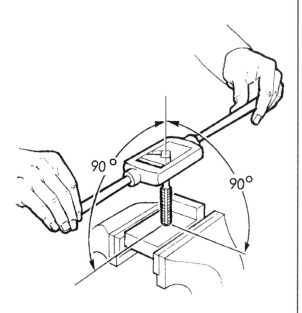

... continued on next page

133

Screw threads - tapping

- Once the taper tap has cut two or three full turns into the hole, the cutting should be continued by giving the tap approximately half a turn forward followed by about a quarter turn backwards. This will break away the cuttings.

- Repeat this forward and backward turning motion until the tap passes through the workpiece or the required depth is reached. Take care not to use excessive force which might break the tap and in a blind hole ensure that the tap is not forced against the bottom. If tapping a blind hole, remove the tap from time to time to clear cuttings from the flutes and from the bottom of the hole.

- Replace the taper tap with an intermediate tap and run this through the hole, again using a half turn forward followed by a small turn backward. If the intermediate tap can pass right through the workpiece the threading is then complete - there is no need to use a plug tap on through holes.

- When tapping a blind hole it is necessary to follow the intermediate tap with a plug tap to take the thread at the bottom of the hole to full size.

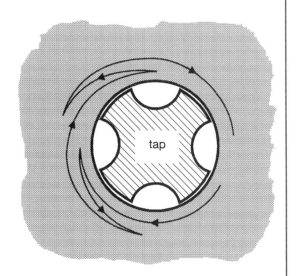

Screw threads - tapping

Hand tapping using a drilling machine

A drilling machine with a centre mounted in the chuck can be used to align and steady the tap as it is turned by hand. Follow the tap with the centre but do not apply any downward force; let the tap screw itself into the hole.

If the hole has just been drilled on the drilling machine and the workpiece is still clamped in position, this technique will give exact alignment of the tap.

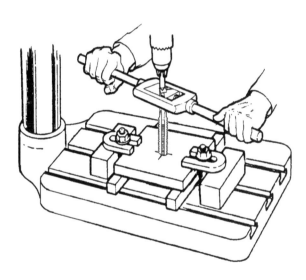

Screw threads - external threading

External threading

A die is used to cut external threads by hand. The most usual type of die is a button die. These are made of high quality tool steel, suitably heat treated.

Dies are available for each size of all the different standard thread forms. There are also dies available for cutting left-hand threads.

One side of the die has the cutting threads tapered a little to provide a lead. This assists with starting the die.

Care must be taken to keep dies in good condition. They are very brittle and can be damaged easily. After use, a die should be carefully cleaned and stored in a suitably partitioned box.

Before using a die examine it carefully. Do not use a chipped die.

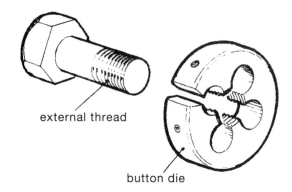

external thread

button die

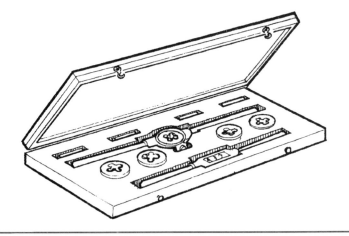

Screw threads - external threading

Die stock

Button dies are held in a die stock. A die stock, like a tap wrench, has two handles which enable the turning force to be applied while holding the die in line with the workpiece. The die should be inserted in the stock with the tapered lead away from the shoulder of the stock.

The die stock has three screws which are used to spring the die open or shut by a small amount. If the two outer screws on the stock are slackened and the central screw is tightened, the die will be forced open. If the central screw is slackened and the two outer screws tightened, the die will close slightly.

The button die should be fully open for the first cut and then reduced to the finishing size. For larger diameter threads it may be desirable to do a first cut, followed by one or more intermediate cuts, and then a finishing cut.

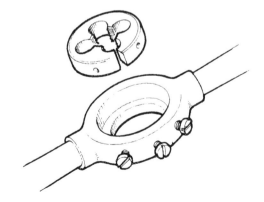

Screw threads - external threading

Using dies

- Check that the workpiece to be threaded is the correct diameter. The blank should be equal to or just slightly larger than the major diameter of the thread required. The end of the blank should be chamfered slightly to give the die a start - see illustration.

- Hold the workpiece securely in a vice or by some other suitable means. If at all possible the part to be threaded should be held vertically.

- Use the adjusting screws on the stock to open up the die to give a shallow cut.

- Place the tapered side of the die squarely on the chamfered end of the workpiece and rotate it in a clockwise direction. Fairly heavy pressure will be needed to start the thread, but once the die begins to cut ease off the pressure and let the die screw itself onto the workpiece.

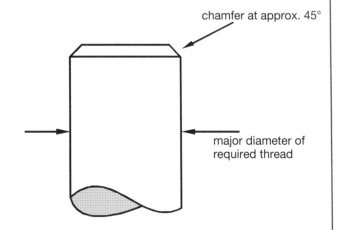

chamfer at approx. 45°

major diameter of required thread

Screw threads - external threading

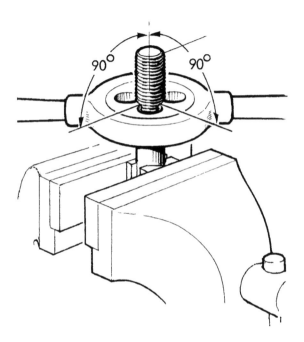

- Great care must be taken to start the thread true to the axis of the blank and the die must be kept square to the axis at all times - see illustration.

- Apply oil or some other suitable lubricant and continue turning the die with an occasional backward rotation to break away the cuttings. Continue until the required length of thread has been cut.

- Turn the die back to the start of the thread and use the adjusting screws on the stock to tighten the die to give a deeper cut.

- Continue the process, tightening the die and recutting the thread, until the thread is of the required diameter.

Since a tap is not adjustable but a die is, it is usual to use the internal thread as the ''master'' and cut the external thread to suit. For general purpose jobbing work a standard nut of the appropriate size and thread form can be used as a gauge. When greater precision is required the threads should be checked against screw thread gauges.

Screw threads - external threading

Half dies

These are in two separate parts which fit into a special stock. The two parts are supplied as a matched pair and it is important that they are always used together. Their separation, and therefore the depth of thread cut, is controlled by an adjusting screw on the stock.

Half dies have the advantage of being adjustable over a wider range than button dies.

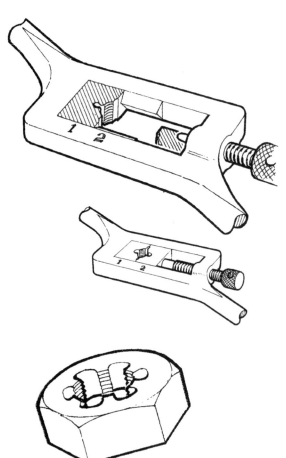

Die nuts

These have no adjustment. They are used for cleaning up damaged threads or bringing a thread which is slightly oversize to the correct size. They are not suitable for cutting new threads.

Limits and fits

When making assemblies of several parts, the dimensions and tolerances of the individual parts have to be specified carefully if the parts are to fit together satisfactorily. The extreme size of a particular dimension is called a limit and the "tightness" with which parts fit together is called the fit.

Limits & fits - limits

Limits

The largest acceptable size for a particular dimension is known as the "high limit". The smallest acceptable size for the same dimension is called the "low limit". The difference between the high and low limits is known as the "tolerance".

When two components are to be fitted together, such as a shaft and a bearing, the difference between the high limit of the inside component and the low limit of the surrounding component is known as the "allowance".

The allowance is the smallest clearance which can occur between the two components when assembled. The largest clearance which can occur is equal to the total of the allowance, the tolerance of the inside component and the tolerance of the outside component.

This permitted difference in size for the two components determines the class of "fit" between the mating parts.

Note: the tolerances and allowance are very small compared with the overall size - the drawing on this page is exaggerated for clarity.

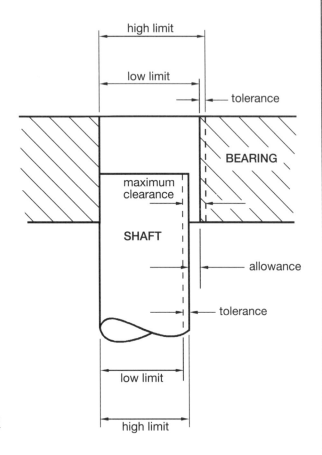

Limits & fits - limits

Limit gauges

Whether or not a component conforms to the specified dimensional limits can be checked using normal measuring instruments. However, for batch and production work it is better to use limit gauges. These are quicker to use, require less skill and are often more accurate.

Limit gauges do not measure actual dimensions but only check that the component is within the specified limits. They are precision instruments and must be handled with care. The checking faces must not be allowed to get damaged and they should be checked regularly against a standard.

The most common types of limit gauge are plug gauges and calliper or snap gauges. There are also gauges for checking screw threads, tapers, profiles etc.

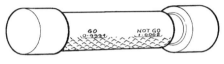

a double-ended plug gauge

a simple calliper gauge

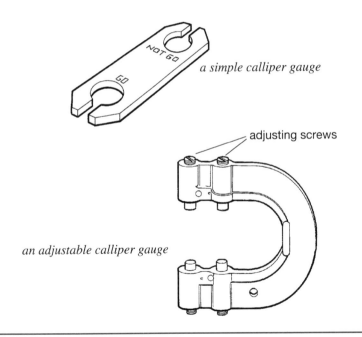

adjusting screws

an adjustable calliper gauge

143

Limits & fits - limits

Plug gauge

This gauge is used for checking that holes and bores are within the specified tolerance.

A typical plug gauge has two machined diameters, one on each end - see illustration on the previous page. The "go" end of the gauge is machined so that it will just fit into a hole equal to the low limit required and the "not-go" end is machined so that it is very slightly larger than the high limit required. For a hole to be within tolerance it must accept the go end of the gauge and not accept the not-go end.

Use the plug gauge as follows.

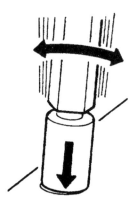

- Clean both the gauge and the hole to be checked, taking particular care that there is no grit or swarf which could damage the gauge.

- Try to insert the go end of the gauge into the hole. Line up the gauge with the axis of the hole and apply slight pressure, rocking it gently backwards and forwards to help it locate. Never use force which might damage the gauge.

- Check that the gauge will pass along the full length of the hole. When checking a blind hole, mark the depth of the hole on the shank of the gauge in pencil to be certain that the gauge goes to the full depth. For blind holes it may be necessary to use a vented gauge to allow the air to escape.

- If the go end of the gauge will not enter the hole satisfactorily the hole is too small and the workpiece needs to be modified or rejected.

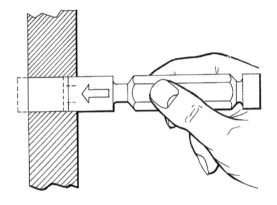

- Now try to insert the not-go end of the gauge into the hole using slight pressure and a gentle rocking motion to help it locate. If the not-go end enters the hole, the hole is oversize and the workpiece should be rejected.

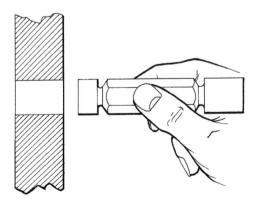

Limits & fits - limits

Calliper gauge (or snap gauge)

These are used to check that external dimensions are within the upper and lower limits. There are two pairs of gauging surfaces (see illustrations here and on page 143). The outer pair are a distance apart equal to the higher limit and the inner pair are set to just prevent the lower limit passing through. The distance between the gauging surfaces can usually be varied over a small range by using adjusting screws. The setting should be checked from time to time.

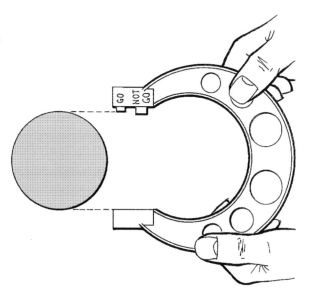

For a diameter or thickness to be within tolerance it must pass between the outer gauging surfaces but not pass between the inner ones. Use a calliper gauge as follows.

- Clean both the gauge and workpiece, taking particular care that there is no grit or swarf that could damage the gauge.

- Offer the gauge to the workpiece. Hold the bottom of the gauge still and rock the top from side to side while pushing it gently onto the workpiece. This searches for the minimum dimension across the diameter or thickness.

- The workpiece is within tolerance if it passes between the outer gauging surfaces but will not pass between the inner gauging surfaces.

Screw thread gauges

There are limit gauges made specifically for checking screw threads. They are more complex than the gauges used for plain dimensions since they have to check the form of the thread as well as the size. Some typical screw thread gauges are shown in the illustrations.

The screw thread calliper gauge shown below can be adjusted to gauge different tolerances.

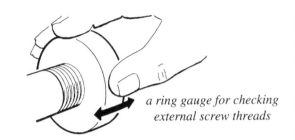

a ring gauge for checking external screw threads

a double-ended plug gauge for checking internal screw threads

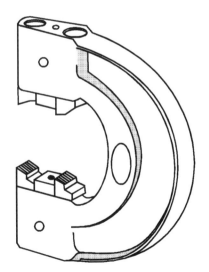

screw thread calliper gauges

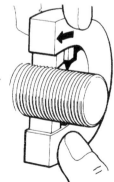

Limits & fits - fits

Fits

When two components have to be assembled together, such as a bearing and a shaft, the difference in size determines the class of "fit". There are three classes of fit: clearance, transition and interference.

Clearance fit

Clearance fits can be further divided into "running" and "free running". Components which have clearance fit can be assembled together by light hand pressure or even without any force at all.

Consider a shaft and a bearing of nominal diameter 30mm with the tolerances shown in the diagram. If both parts are within the stated tolerances, the hole must always be at least 0.025mm larger than the shaft and could be as much as 0.080mm. This will enable the components to be fitted together easily and is typical of a clearance fit.

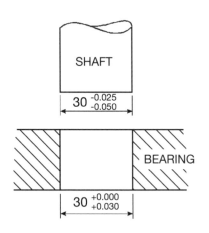

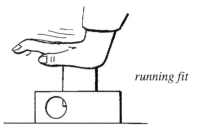

running fit

free running fit

Transition fit

This can be sub-divided into "light press" and "push" fits. As the tolerances are such that the parts may have slight interference or a very small clearance, they may need a light press or taps from a hammer to assemble them.

Consider a shaft and a bearing of nominal diameter 30mm with the tolerances shown in the diagram. If both parts are within the stated tolerances, the shaft may be up to 0.018mm larger than the hole or as much as 0.016mm smaller than the hole. This sort of variation is typical of a transition fit.

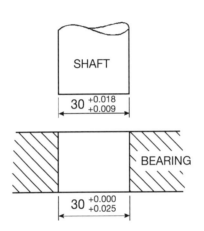

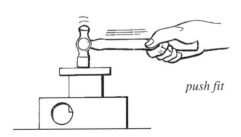

push fit

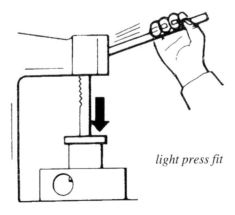

light press fit

149

Limits & fits - fits

Interference fit

This can also be referred to as a "drive", "press" or "force" fit. The inner component is always larger than the outer component and assembly can only be achieved by the application of considerable force.

Consider a shaft and a bearing of nominal diameter 30mm with the tolerances shown in the diagram. If both parts are within the stated tolerances, the shaft will be between 0.001mm and 0.042mm larger than the hole. These dimensions are typical of an interference fit.

There is an extreme interference fit called a "shrink" fit. This is when the shaft is so much larger than the hole that it cannot be assembled by the application of force alone. Assembly is achieved by heating the outer component so that it expands. The cold shaft is forced into the heat expanded hole, which is then shrunk onto the shaft by cooling. This technique is used for fixing railway wagon wheels onto their axles.

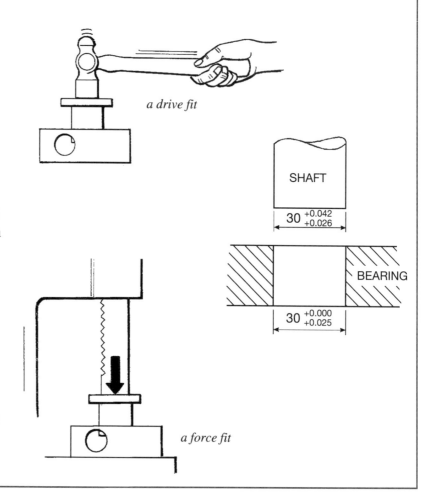

a drive fit

SHAFT

$30 \, ^{+0.042}_{+0.026}$

BEARING

$30 \, ^{+0.000}_{+0.025}$

a force fit

150

Limits & fits - ISO system

ISO system

There is an ISO system for specifying fit between shafts and bearings or similar mating components. A brief description of the system is given below, but refer to BS 4500 for further details.

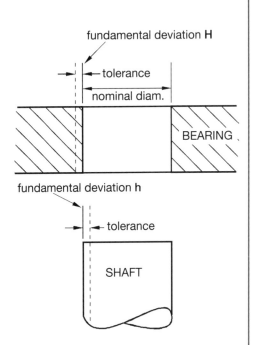

The outer component (the bearing or hole) is described by a capital letter followed by a number, eg **H6**. The inner component (the shaft) is described by a lower case letter followed by a number, eg **h6**.

The letters specify the fundamental deviation of the actual dimensions from the nominal dimensions - this is sometimes called the "tolerance position". The letter **H** (and also **h**) specifies zero fundamental deviation, in other words the tolerance ranges from the nominal size.

Example: An **h6** shaft of nominal diameter 25mm can
vary between 24.987mm and 25.000mm

Note, however, that an **H6** bearing (or hole) of nominal diameter 25mm can vary between 25.000mm and 25.013mm. The tolerance on both shaft and bearing is in the direction which increases clearance between the two. The shaft can be smaller than its fundamental deviation by the amount of the tolerance and the hole can be larger than its fundamental deviation by the amount of the tolerance.

151

Limits & fits - ISO system

On the previous page we considered bearings and shafts for which the fundamental deviation was zero (**H** and **h**). This combination can never give a shaft which is larger than the bearing; the shaft can be the same size as the bearing or smaller by the amount of the tolerances. The fit will always be clearance.

Tighter or looser fits can be specified by moving the fundamental deviation of either the shaft or the bearing, or both. Letters beyond **H** in the alphabet specify a shift of fundamental deviation to always give oversize shafts and undersize holes. The further the designating letter is from **H** the greater the amount of oversize in the shaft or undersize in the hole and therefore the tighter the fit.

For a 25mm diameter shaft, the table below gives examples of the **minimum** diameters that are within tolerance for different fundamental deviations:

ISO Designating Letter	h	k	n	p	s
Minimum Diameter mm	25.000	25.002	25.015	25.022	25.035

Note that the actual value of fundamental deviation for each designating letter varies with the nominal diameter of the shaft - see the table on the next page.

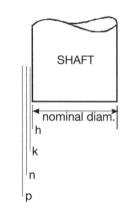

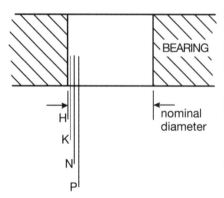

Note: the fundamental deviations are very small - the drawing is exaggerated for clarity

Limits & fits - ISO system

Conversely, an ISO designating letter that comes before **H** in the alphabet specifies a shift of fundamental deviation in the direction which gives undersize shafts and oversize holes - a looser fit.

For a 25mm diameter shaft, the table below gives examples of the **maximum** diameters that are within tolerance for different fundamental deviations.

ISO Designating Letter	d	e	f	g	h
Fundamental Deviation mm	0.065	0.040	0.020	0.007	0.000
Maximum Diameter mm	24.935	24.960	24.980	24.993	25.000

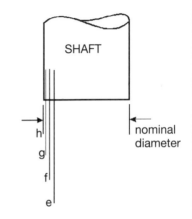

SHAFT

nominal diameter

The actual value of fundamental deviation designated by each letter varies with the nominal diameter of the shaft or hole. *Examples:*

ISO Designating Letter	FUNDAMENTAL DEVIATION mm		
	Nominal Diameter of Hole or Shaft		
	25mm	60mm	100mm
D or d	0.065	0.100	0.120
E or e	0.040	0.060	0.072
F or f	0.020	0.030	0.036
G or g	0.007	0.010	0.012
H or h	0.000	0.000	0.000
K or k	0.002	0.002	0.003
N or n	0.015	0.020	0.023

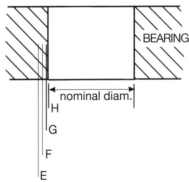

BEARING

nominal diam.

*Note: the deviations are positive for holes and negative for shafts for letters **A** to **G**. For letters after **H** the signs are reversed - negative for holes and positive for shafts.*

Limits & fits - ISO system

Tolerances

In the ISO system, the number which follows the fundamental deviation letter specifies the tolerance which is acceptable. The tolerance is the amount of variation which is permitted between individual parts made to the same specification. The combination of nominal size, fundamental deviation and tolerance specifies the maximum and minimum dimensions which are acceptable.

The number specifying tolerance is on a scale **1** to **16** - the smaller the number the tighter the tolerance. The value of the tolerance for each designating number varies with the diameter of the shaft or hole. The table gives examples of tolerance for three particular sizes of shaft.

Note that the tolerance ranges from the fundamental deviation in a direction away from the nominal size - see diagram. This applies for both shafts and bearings (holes).

ISO Tolerance Number	TOLERANCE mm		
	Nominal Diameter of Shaft		
	25mm	60mm	100mm
6	0.013	0.019	0.022
7	0.021	0.030	0.035
8	0.033	0.046	0.054
9	0.052	0.074	0.087
10	0.084	0.120	0.140
11	0.130	0.190	0.220

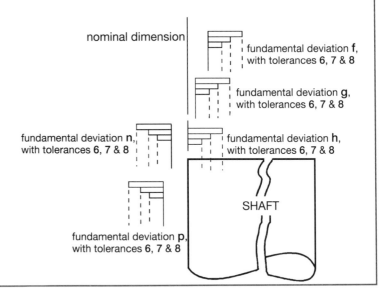

nominal dimension

fundamental deviation **f**, with tolerances 6, 7 & 8

fundamental deviation **g**, with tolerances 6, 7 & 8

fundamental deviation **n**, with tolerances 6, 7 & 8

fundamental deviation **h**, with tolerances 6, 7 & 8

SHAFT

fundamental deviation **p**, with tolerances 6, 7 & 8

Limits & fits - ISO system

Fits

In the ISO system, the fit of a shaft and a bearing is described by stating the designation of the hole followed by the designation of the shaft.

Example: **H8 - e7** or **H8/e7**

A bearing of nominal size 25mm and **H8** specification will have a minimum size of 25.000mm and a maximum size of 25.033mm. This is made up of zero fundamental deviation and a tolerance of 0.033mm.

A shaft of nominal size 25mm and **e7** specification will have a maximum size of 24.960mm and a minimum size of 24.939mm. This is made up of a fundamental deviation of 0.040mm and a tolerance of 0.021mm.

This combination will give a clearance fit. The minimum clearance will be 0.040mm and the maximum clearance will be 0.094mm, depending upon where the individual components lie within the range of tolerance.

Now you use the data given in the tables on pages 153 &154 to work out answers to the following. Write your answers in the boxes.

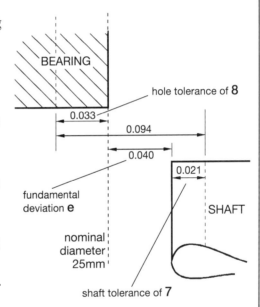

1. Shaft and hole with nominal diameter 60mm, ISO fit **H8/e7**

2. Shaft and hole with nominal diameter 25mm, ISO fit **H7/g6**

	Maximum clearance	Minimum clearance

Off-hand grinding

The off-hand grinder is used for sharpening and reconditioning a wide range of tools when high accuracy in the grinding is not necessary. The article being ground is held in the hand. The amount of grinding and the angles generated are regulated by eye. When the grinding is finished the results can be checked against gauges.

Off-hand grinding - safety

Safety

Grinding wheels can be very dangerous if proper precautions are not taken.

A major danger is from a wheel breaking or bursting while revolving. Grinding wheels generally revolve at high speed and pieces which break off can be ejected with considerable force.

Another danger comes from the small particles which fly off during the normal grinding process. These can include fragments of jagged metal, particularly when grinding a mushroomed head off a chisel.

As with any other power driven equipment, there is also a danger of loose clothing or hair becoming entangled in the moving parts.

a bursting grinding wheel can
cause severe injury if not properly guarded

Off-hand grinding - safety

Before starting any grinding operation:

- wear suitable safety goggles - THIS IS ABSOLUTELY ESSENTIAL

- ensure that you have no loose clothing or hair which could get caught up in the grinding wheel

- inspect the grinding wheel for surface defects and check that it has an even face and sides

- check that the tool rest, the guards and the screen are correctly positioned in relation to the grinding wheel

- stand to one side when starting the grinding wheel

- check that the wheel is running true.

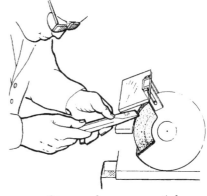

safety goggles are essential when grinding

Abrasive Wheel Regulations (1970)

These Regulations require that abrasive wheels (grinding wheels) may only be mounted by persons who have received training in accordance with the Regulations and are appointed for the purpose.

Do not attempt to mount or replace a grinding wheel yourself unless you have been trained and appointed for the purpose. If you have any doubt about the condition of a grinding wheel do not use it but report it to your supervisor or instructor.

Off-hand grinding - machines

Machines

An off-hand grinding machine is essentially an electric motor with a grinding wheel mounted directly onto the spindle. It is common to have two grinding wheels, one on each side of the drive motor. The two grinding wheels will have different grinding characteristics. One will be used for rough grinding and the other for finer grinding.

An off-hand grinding machine can be mounted on a bench or on a pedestal fixed to the floor. These are often called bench grinding machines and pedestal grinding machines.

Pedestal grinding machines sometimes have a small tank fixed to the front of the pedestal. This is for holding water or some other suitable quenching (cooling) fluid. Grinding generates quite a lot of heat in the workpiece and it is necessary to cool it from time to time. If the workpiece is not kept sufficiently cool the temper of the metal may be destroyed.

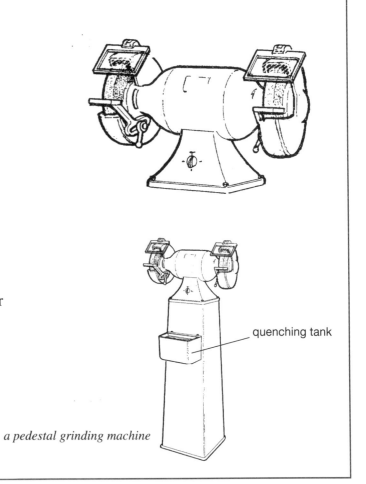

quenching tank

a pedestal grinding machine

Off-hand grinding - machines

The grinding wheel is made of abrasive particles bonded together. Most wheels used on off-hand grinders are made from silicon carbide (carborundum), but aluminium oxide abrasives are sometimes used for fine grinding.

About three-quarters of the circumference of the grinding wheel is encased in the wheel guard. In addition there is a screen. This is adjustable and should be used to cover as much of the exposed part of the wheel as possible without interfering with the grinding operation.

The tool should be adjusted so that there is just a small gap between it and the grinding wheel. If the gap is too large there is a danger of something (such as your finger!) becoming trapped between the tool rest and the revolving wheel.

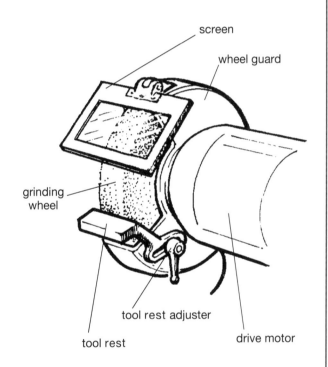

screen

wheel guard

grinding wheel

tool rest adjuster

tool rest

drive motor

Tool grinding

Grinding a chisel

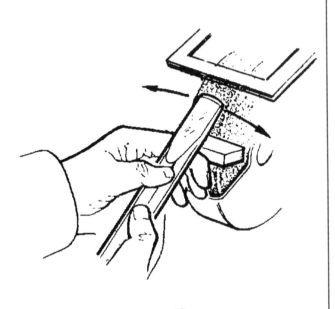

- Check the existing angles on the chisel to see that they are correct (a 60° cutting edge is normal).

- Hold the chisel in one hand and support that hand against the tool rest with the cutting edge of the chisel at an angle of 60° to the grinding wheel.

- Hold the head of the chisel in the other hand and guide the cutting edge backwards and forwards, slowly and lightly across the face of the wheel.

- Turn the chisel over and grind the other side of the cutting edge in the same way.

- Check the angle of the cutting edge using a centre gauge.

Note: the cutting edge should be kept cool by quenching at frequent intervals.

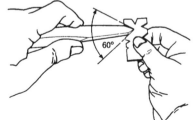

Off-hand grinding - tool grinding

Mushroomed heads on chisels are dangerous and should be removed. The head of a chisel should be flat with a chamfer.

Removing a mushroomed head should be done on a coarse grinding wheel.

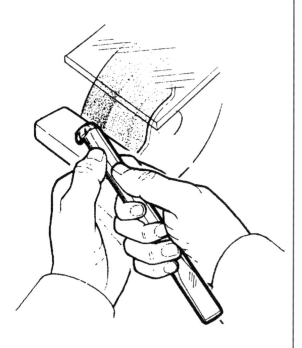

- Hold the chisel in both hands, as shown in the illustration, with one hand steadied against the tool rest.

- Rotate the head of the chisel against the grinding wheel with the chisel more or less horizontal and at an angle of approximately 20° or 30° to the axis of the wheel.

- Apply only a light pressure at first. As the jagged edge of the mushroomed head becomes smoother and rounder, the pressure can be increased.

- Continue, quenching as necessary, until all the splayed metal has been removed and a correct chamfer has been formed.

- It may also be necessary to grind the top of the chisel flat and at a right angle to the axis of the chisel.

Caution: when grinding a mushroomed head quite large fragments of jagged metal can fly off.

Off-hand grinding - tool grinding

Grinding a centre punch

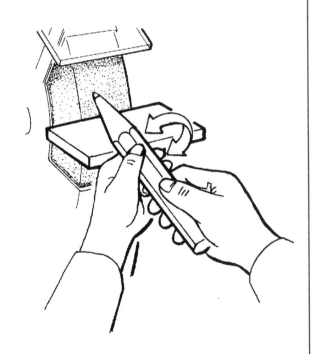

- Hold the centre punch in one hand and position the fingers of the other hand on the head of the punch so that they can rotate it.

- Steady the first hand against the tool rest and adjust the angle of the punch so that it is held at approximately 60° to the face of the wheel.

- Touch the point of the punch to the grinding wheel and rotate it against the wheel. Keep a light even pressure against the wheel while rotating the punch.

- Do not allow the point of the punch to become overheated as this will soften the metal. Quench the punch frequently in a suitable coolant.

- When the grinding operation is finished, check that the point of the punch is concentric (centred on the axis).

Note: the point of a punch should always be ground with the grinding lines parallel to the axis. Transverse grinding weakens the point.

Off-hand grinding - tool grinding

Grinding a twist drill

• Check the existing angles ground onto the drill tip and decide whether they are correct or need adjustment. If the angles are correct they can be used to guide the regrinding process.

• Let the drill rest on the left hand with approximately 40mm of the tip extended. Grasp the shank of the drill with the other hand.

• Hold the drill horizontally and present one of the cutting edges of the drill to the grinding wheel in such a way that it is parallel with the face of the wheel. Steady the left hand against the tool rest and lightly touch the drill cutting edge to the grinding wheel.

• While applying light forward pressure into the grinding wheel, lower the hand grasping the shank of the drill and at the same time turn the drill slightly clockwise (see lower illustrations). This will grind the lip clearance angle onto the drill.

• Repeat the two previous stages as necessary until the required angles and clearances are achieved, quenching the drill as necessary.

• While keeping the left hand in exactly the same position, rotate the drill through 180° and grind the second cutting edge to match the first.

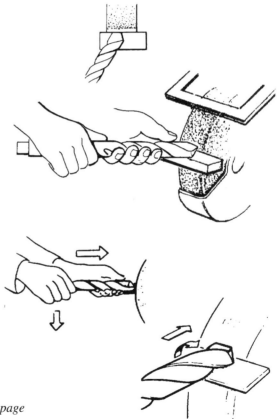

... continued on next page

165

Off-hand grinding - tool grinding

When the twist drill has been reground, check the lip angles using a grinding gauge. The standard point angle for a twist drill is 118°, that is 59° either side of the centre line. However, different angles may be required for special applications - see page 78.

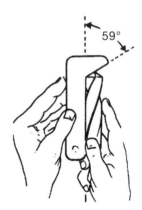

Also check the drill point corners using a gauge, as follows:

- rub chalk on the back face of the gauge

- position the shank of the drill on the point of the gauge and scribe a line on the chalked face with the corner of one of the drill cutting edges

- turn the drill through 180° and scribe a second line using the corner of the other cutting edge.

The position of the two lines should coincide. If they do not, the drill should be reground.

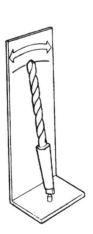

Off-hand grinding - tool grinding

It is sometimes necessary to thin the point of a twist drill.

- Hold the drill firmly with both hands.

- Present one heel edge of the drill to the corner of the grinding wheel while holding the drill at an angle to the vertical.

- Apply light pressure to thin the point, taking care that the cutting edge of the drill does not touch the grinding wheel.

- Repeat the process on the other side of the drill.

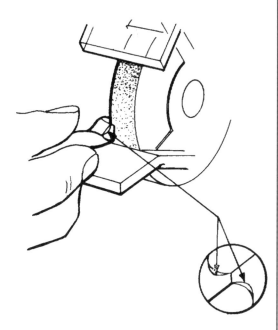

168

Index

Index

Index

Index

ANSWERS TO QUESTIONS ON PAGE 155

1. A shaft and hole with nominal diameter 60mm and ISO fit **H8/e7** will have:

Maximum clearance	0.136mm
Minimum clearance	0.060mm

2. A shaft and hole of nominal diameter 25mm and ISO fit **H7/g6** will have:

Maximum clearance	0.041mm
Minimum clearance	0.007mm

Notes

Notes

Notes

Notes